Praise for B

Is this the desert island book on lean? If you have the goal of improving design and construction, I can think of no better operating manual than *Better Building: Lean Practice for the Project-Driven Organization*. Klaus pulls together philosophy, culture, tools and structure in a very well-crafted book. His six core practices are practical and comprehensible; together they could serve a lifetime of improvement as well as an intriguing introduction. His examples are engagingly drawn from real life and balance some strong theory. The book motivates me to act, to improve.

—Stan Chiu, Principal at HGA Architects

Klaus Lemke has made a significant contribution to the body of critical knowledge helping us all apply lean thinking within the construction industry. *Better Building: Lean Practice for the Project-Driven Organization* is an easy-to-read, comprehensive, and practical book that applies the principles of lean operations to the nuances and challenges of construction projects and construction industry companies. Throughout the book, Klaus offers simple advice and examples that will improve your project delivery, raise team performance, deliver more value to your customers, and strengthen your organization.

—Tim Reimann, Executive Vice President of Operations
at McGough

Better Building is an excellent, practical guide on what we can do to improve how we work together to deliver projects in the building industry. Klaus has gone beyond the tools to describe the underlying challenges that face our industry, and the practices through which we can at least start to address them. He draws from his depth of experience, using real stories from real projects, to show how subtle changes in how we collaborate can bring dramatic improvements. *Better Building* translates "Lean" for the AEC industry like no other book has, and is a must read for leaders who want to improve the way we work.

— **Dean Cook, Senior Director of Lean at Mortenson**

Klaus Lemke is a skilled builder, a blend of a theoretician whose head is above the clouds and a practitioner whose feet are firmly rooted in the ground. Not only does he bridge theory and practice—he also fuses his long-term view of the True North with attention to the details of the building teams' daily work.

Lemke presents a useful guide for anyone who seeks to produce building processes that answer to the specific needs of the customer. He pays particular attention to the transformation from a bureaucratic, inflexible hierarchically-structured organization to an organization that recruits and engages a building community made up of multi-skilled working teams according to the unique building process—and thus adapts itself with agility to the circumstances of time, place, and the needs of the customer. The book deals with construction, yet the principles of management required in order to cope with a complex construction project under conditions of uncertainty will be of use to anyone who seeks to deal with processes of product design and development, technologies, processes and human capabilities.

This book provides a window onto the learning process of human creation. This process begins with a purpose—human meaning and need, vision which is then translated into a tangible artifact, continues as the foundation of committed shared values are laid and the scaffolding made out of the principles of lean thinking is erected. In the end, it provides a common language (protocols and standards), which will protect the project and ensure that it does not collapse or degenerate into a biblical Tower of Babylon.

—**Boaz Tamir, Founder and President of Israel Lean Enterprise (ILE)**

What happens when a bright young structural engineer becomes a passionate builder of challenging structures in a highly collaborative environment, and later adopts a mindset of protecting only his employer's interests, before finally discovering lean and becoming a Lean Construction teacher and guide? You get a clear, practical and insightful book on building better as a lean thinker. This book provides a comprehensive and actionable model that can help any owner, designer or builder improve their teams and outcomes. You can take advantage of this good fortune by studying Klaus Lemke's book, *Better Building: Lean Practice for the Project-Driven Organization.*

—**Dean Reed, Lean Integration Advocate, Organizer & Educator at DPR Construction**

In *Better Building*, Klaus Lemke generously offers lessons learned from his experience with traditional project management and his personal transition to lean practices in engineering and construction. He focuses on developing lean project teams, stressing that personnel from different companies are bound to deliver their project together and therefore, as a team, must develop their lean behaviors and adopt lean tools in unison. As a lean project coach for more than 10 years, he has helped numerous project teams overcome their skepticism and reluctance to fully deploy lean practices on their projects and in their organizations. If you doubt that lean can be successfully applied to the one-of-a-kind work of design and construction, this book will change your mind.

—Iris D. Tommelein, Professor,
Director of the Project Production Systems Laboratory,
Civil and Environmental Engineering Dept.,
Univ. of California, Berkeley

Better Building

Lean Practice for
the Project-Driven Organization

Klaus Lemke

LeanProject PUBLISHING

Better Building: Lean Practice for the Project-Driven Organization
By Klaus Lemke

Published by

 LeanProject PUBLISHING

ISBN: 978-0-9998783-1-6 (print)

BUSINESS & ECONOMICS / Management

Original cover art by Bill Blanski, FAIA, Design Principal with HGA
Book design by Nick Zelinger, NZ Graphics

QUANTITY PURCHASES: Schools, companies, professional groups, clubs, and other organizations may qualify for special terms when ordering quantities of this title.

For information, email publishing@leanproject.com.

Disclaimer: LeanProject Publishing and the Author make no representation or warranty that any of the content of this book will ensure successful results for the reader and its content should be solely considered as the Company's and the Author's best advice based on the current knowledge available to them at the time of its publication. Some names and details have been changed for flow and to protect the anonymity of our clients and individuals.

Printed in the United States of America

To my dad for teaching me how to snap a chalk line
and bait a hook,

and

to my wife, Heidi, for everything else.

CONTENTS

Foreword by Greg Howell v

Introduction 1

    What's Broken in Building 5

    A Better Way to Work 6

    Better Building 7

    How to Read This Book 10

Chapter 1 – Long-Term Thinking for a Short-Term World . . . 15

    Why Think Long-Term 16

    A Tale of Two Developers 18

    Deploy Strategy to the Project Level 26

Chapter 2 – Conquering Variability 33

    Minimize Variation to Maximize Workflow 36

    Design Work Processes to Accommodate Variability
    That Remains 44

    Plan and Execute Work in Small Batches 45

    Use Visible Buffers That the Team Shares 50

    Make Decisions and Plans at the Last
    Responsible Moment 52

Chapter 3 – Fast-Launching Teams 57

    Rocket vs. Airplane 58

    Visual Management Sets the Stage 60

    Leaders Must Model the Right Behavior
    (and Recruit Followers) 64

    Followers Are Key to Success (Why Dread Pirate Roberts
    Will Live Forever) 67

Onboarding on Purpose 69

Experiential Learning 71

Learning Through Practice 73

Improving and Maintaining Together 75

Conclusion 76

**Chapter 4 – Developing Your Temporary People
and Partners** 77

Learn with Your Partners, Not Before Them 90

Ask Your Partners to Help Model New Habits 91

Practice Making Improvements Together 92

Chapter 5 – Leading Without Authority 95

The Leadership Behavior Matrix 96

Reliance on Authority 97

Level of Demonstrated Respect for People 98

Commander 100

Influencer 101

Delegator 101

Mentor 102

Traditional Leadership Behavior Profile 103

Exponential Leadership Behavior Profile 108

Shifting from Traditional to Exponential Leadership 111

Chapter 6 – Learn Through Fearless Experimentation 119

Set Powerful Objectives 124

Use Short Learning Cycles 127

Learn on Value-Added Work 129

Control the Risk 132

Experiment at All Levels 137

Chapter 7 – Leading Change 141

    Know Where You Are 143

    Set Clear Goals 148

    Expect Resistance 150

    Practice Leadership at Every Level 152

    Change Routines to Change Thinking 155

Chapter 8 – Lean Tools for Project Work 159

    Last Planner® System (Including Pull Planning) 164

    A3 Problem Solving 167

    Visual Management (Including 5S Programs) 168

    Quick Wins 170

    Choosing by Advantages Decision-Making 171

    Integrated Project Delivery 173

    Conclusion 176

About the Author 177

About Lean Project Consulting, Inc 179

Foreword
by Greg Howell

PEOPLE OFTEN ASK me about the path we've taken to get where we are today with lean construction. Well, it certainly wasn't because I had a clear roadmap or any strong idea of where we were going. I feel more like I've been part of a series of fortunate accidents and personal connections that let me be part of something very important and powerful in the industry. As I learned about and worked in the construction industry, I was repeatedly struck with the idea that the Critical Path Method, while useful, was deeply flawed as a tool for planning and executing work. Although it was widely accepted as THE way to manage construction projects, it seemed to me that CPM was ineffective for dealing with a world full of so much variation, uncertainty, and disconnectedness.

I was fortunate to meet Glenn Ballard, who first asked the question, "How well does planning work?" My response was, "I don't know, let's find out." This conversation was the beginning of some experiments around foreman planning that eventually led us to early versions of the Last Planner® System. As Glenn and I continued to experiment, a small group formed, which included Lauri Koskela and Iris Tommmelein. Together we continued challenging the current thinking about project planning and execution. Hal Macomber brought the work of Fernando Flores and the Language Action Perspective to the discussion, highlighting the need for reliable promising and viewing every project as a network of commitments. He also developed the Study Action Team™ approach to open up conversations and speed up organizational learning.

In my recollection, it was not about creating an overnight revolution. We were working to make the process of building better – one experiment at a time. Some succeeded and others failed, and we kept moving forward. Along the way, we connected with many others who were willing to experiment and try new things together. It was this group of connected open-minded thinkers that made the difference and still moves the industry forward today.

There were definitely roadblocks along the way. The established ideas around project management were firmly rooted in the industry, and we were trying to disrupt the core beliefs of most industry experts. I remember speaking to a large audience about the idea that the current theory of project management was obsolete. At the end of my presentation, I was afraid I'd be run out of town by a mob. For a handful of audience members, the provocation opened a new discussion. Several of those people would become influential in the lean construction movement.

Resistance to change, and the rigid beliefs of industry leaders were always our biggest hurdles. We didn't spend a lot of time focused on the resistors. We engaged with anyone who wanted to be part of a change and continued to build energy for something new.

While there is still much to do in transforming the industry, we have proven that these concepts work in construction. Planning and executing projects with multi-disciplinary teams makes sense, and we see it succeed with techniques like the Last Planner System and Integrated Project Delivery. Some organizations have put this thinking in the middle of their operations and they're getting consistently better results. Those who are serious and willing to change their thinking are transforming how project work gets done and leading the way for the rest.

I still see a lot of confusion in the industry, mostly from those sitting on the sidelines making decisions about their projects and organizations without jumping in themselves. A common mistake is to think of it as a programmatic fix – that thinking is wrong. This is a shift in mindset. The ones who succeed are willing to suspend disbelief and try experiments. Making sure early efforts succeed is key, and this means engaging the "crusty superintendent" who's not interested in change. We have had good success with simulations and games that help them experience the change themselves and realize there could be another way. Along the way we confirmed our hunch that most of these superintendents weren't so crusty after all.

Too many leaders say they want to be lean but don't invest personally in new thinking. They say the right things but stick with their old-school ideology when the chips are down. I can think of several companies that idled in that place for many years before actually making real change, sometimes only after a change in leadership.

Changing the way people think and behave on projects is tough and "the way we do things around here" is hard to change. I can only say that the progress we made was by connecting people and trying experiments. Take every opportunity to connect to others who are trying to make a difference; then get to work.

Klaus Lemke has written a valuable book, a book that will change how you see, understand, and act on projects. Read it and ask your team to read it. Study it together. Klaus makes the thinking behind lean easy to understand and keeps the focus on learning in practice. Don't worry that you don't know where it will all end, just take another step and try another experiment. This book will help you do just that.

Greg Howell

Lean Construction Pioneer and

Co-Founder of the Lean Construction Institute

Introduction

"Just keep your head down, and it'll be over before you know it." That was the advice from my co-workers in the design office at Chicago Bridge & Iron as I prepared to enter a nine-month stint working within the company's construction arm. I was the new hire structural engineer and had just about finished my rounds of orientation—making my way through each department to get the sense of the entire company and all its moving parts. The company specialized in the design, fabrication, and construction of large site-constructed heavy plate structures like water towers, oil storage tanks, and large pressure vessels. I had finished one year in the design office and three months in the manufacturing plant. All I had left was construction, and then I could return to my permanent position as a structural design engineer, the work I had been hired to do.

My office mates shared war stories that painted construction as the most miserable part of their two-year orientations. The jobsite office trailers were dirty, cramped, and never comfortable—always way too hot or way too cold. They described the construction crews as uncivilized oafs who had shown them no respect and took every opportunity to mock their inexperience or make them look foolish. The project crews were typically comprised of about two dozen highly skilled guys who were really good at what they did, and between work hours lived like a gang of forty-year-old rodeo cowboys—getting drunk, gambling, and sleeping four to a hotel room to save on living expenses. When it was all over, they'd pick up and go on to the next show.

Despite the horror stories, I immediately felt at home on my first construction site, building a series of storage tanks for a new wastewater treatment process at a Toledo refinery. I was traveling with my wife and young sons and had no interest in the rowdy lifestyle but was energized by working with those who were directly adding value for our customers, and grew to appreciate the skill and craftsmanship of every person working on the site. From the foreman to the welders, to the riggers, laborers, and crane operator, each one brought a special expertise that was required to make the project a reality. Although sometimes a little rough around the edges, each person was a true craftsman in their own right, and I felt privileged to do whatever I could to make their work flow more smoothly, whether I was laying out the structures, answering design questions, completing quality checks, or interfacing with our on-site customer. When my nine months were up, I did not go back to the engineering office. I'd found my home in construction.

After a few years in the field, I had a chance to work on our company's partnership with Shell Oil to build all their new storage tanks for their facilities around the world. The partnership was born out of Deming's concept of Total Quality Management,[1] which focused on doing things right the first time, eliminating unnecessary work processes, and continuously improving. The partnership seemed like a reasonable thing to do, since we had already been building about 60 percent of their tanks anyway, and the old process of bidding each project had cost both sides a lot of wasted time and money. The new partnership allowed for pricing transparency and, more importantly, allowed us to eliminate a bunch of expensive wasteful work. The partnership lowered costs for Shell, let us respond faster when they

[1] Mary Welton, *The Deming Management Method: W. Edwards Deming, the Genius Who Revitalized Japanese Industry, Offers His Unorthodox System to Make "Made in America" a Guarantee of Quality—Again!* (New York: Perigee Book, 1986). See for background on Total Quality Management.

needed new tanks in a hurry, and gave us a more reliable workload which helped reduce costs and shorten delivery schedules even further. This way of working together made so much sense to me, I just figured it was how anyone would do it. I had no way of knowing then that there was anything unique about this, or how many other companies didn't do it this way at all. It wasn't until I left the oil industry and went to work for a commercial general contractor that I realized how revolutionary the partnering approach really was.

The commercial construction industry was, and still is, largely a siloed business, with owners, architects, engineers, general contractors, trade contractors, and suppliers each working hard to defend their own profit margins by shifting risk to other parties whenever possible.

I quickly set aside the collaborative approach I had experienced with the Shell partnership and learned to be a very effective project manager in this world, shifting responsibility to subcontractors and suppliers through carefully worded contracts, and making watertight claims to owners for extra costs and time whenever there was a hiccup on one of my projects. I was an expert at providing notices both upstream to the owner and downstream to subcontractors in a way that protected our position without starting a battle. However, if a battle was later necessary, I had built a paper arsenal that assured our victory.

My projects were almost always profitable, but I always felt a little incomplete when working in this way—like I was missing something important. I knew this way of working was horribly inefficient, and that we were missing huge opportunities to do better as an industry. I had gotten a taste of something so much better in my previous job and was determined to get back to that model again . . . someday.

While working toward my MBA in the mid 2000s, I was introduced to the idea of lean manufacturing. I devoured the book *The Toyota*

Way by Jeffrey Liker, which dissected the thinking and tactics that allowed Toyota to surpass their competitors in every measure, and felt like this idea of lean might explain what I'd experienced with Shell Oil and what was missing in the building industry. After all, Toyota's success was built on many of the ideas that Deming had instilled in Japan after World War II. I attended my first Lean Construction Institute Congress in 2005, where I first met Greg Howell and Glenn Ballard. I was in awe of their optimism and ability to overcome the barriers that were so strongly embedded against a new way of thinking and working. I became inspired with the idea that the building industry could adopt a lean way of working.

As I studied lean principles and tried to put them to work on my own projects, I found myself stuck in a world between optimism and frustration. I knew the concepts could work in the building industry, but was having little success making real improvements. The way I felt at the time, and still do sometimes, is best described by one of my favorite quotes. It comes from my wife Heidi, who once remarked, "Give a man a fish and he eats for a day, but teach a man to fish, and he'll be frustrated for life!" The great potential of lean, and the great dysfunctions of the building industry kept me wanting more. The more I learned, the more dissatisfied I became with the status quo.

I finally called Greg Howell several years later with this question about the consulting business: "Is it really possible to focus full-time on improving the building industry, and still make a living?" We talked for only a couple weeks before I decided to join his small firm, Lean Project Consulting, and made the commitment to improving the building industry by applying lean principles. I've learned more about lean, leadership, coaching, and human nature in the six years since than I did in my previous twenty-two in the building industry.

What's Broken in Building

As a consultant, I have the opportunity to work with companies and people in all parts of the United States and even around the world. One exercise we do with almost every new group is to have a discussion about what's not working in the building industry. Whether we are talking to executives responsible for building at a Fortune 100 global company, leaders of a regional general contracting firm, architectural design leaders, or a group of foremen on a jobsite, the replies are remarkably similar. The foremen complain that the other trades are always getting in their way and the project superintendent's schedule is not realistic. The general contractors complain that the architect is not responding quickly enough to requests for information and the owner takes too long to make decisions. The owners complain that the trades are always asking for change orders and schedule extensions even though they have not requested a single design change. Many people complain that the rest of the team is not trustworthy and does not follow through on their commitments. In the end, people feel that the building industry is disjointed, and that work does not flow smoothly from one party to the next. The handoffs are inefficient, and the baton often gets dropped. The list of dissatisfactions confirms what I had experienced firsthand: most problems in design and construction are caused by the spaces between the work, not the work itself.

Historically, the industry has responded by trying to resolve problems through tightening of contract language, defining scopes more precisely, and drawing even sharper lines between parties. The silo walls that are causing the majority of the problems are reinforced and made even taller. One colleague defined the problem quite nicely when he asked, "Did you ever notice that building leaks always occur where two contracts come together?" As much as we might try, it's impossible to solve coordination problems with tighter contracts.

A Better Way to Work

The good news is that there is a better way, and we don't even have to come up with it on our own. We have an excellent model to adopt and adapt. When Toyota's capabilities as a world-class manufacturer became a popular subject with the publishing of *The Machine That Changed the World* in 1990, lean thinking was credited with creating the most improvement in manufacturing since Henry Ford popularized mass production and the moving assembly line.[2] The book was derived from an MIT study about the future of the auto industry and how Toyota was able to outperform the big three US auto manufacturers in nearly every measure. It shined a light on a new way of thinking about manufacturing, something the authors called "lean production."

Since then, lean has influenced virtually every industry in every part of the world. Key lean concepts including continuous improvement and respect for people have been articulated and dissected in countless books and articles since. Much of the writing about lean and the Toyota Production System (TPS) is geared toward applying lean tools and techniques to your own business, whether that's manufacturing, shipbuilding, healthcare, or any other production or service industry.

Liker's 2004 book, *The Toyota Way* was the most thorough attempt yet to break down Toyota's thinking and behaviors so that we could begin to understand what made the company so successful. Liker's book has served as a guide for lean practitioners ever since. One of the reasons that *The Toyota Way* is so compelling is that it acknowledges that lean and TPS are not just a set of tools that can be copied. Success depends on adopting a new way of thinking and an organization-wide culture shift, a lean transformation. Nevertheless, we find lean imitators

---

[2] James P. Womack, Daniel T. Jones, and Daniel Roos, *The Machine That Changed the World*, (New York: Rawson Associates, 1990).

doing their best to copy Toyota's tools without first understanding the thinking and culture behind its success.

Blindly implementing lean tools almost always leads to disappointment and the discovery that these techniques do not work as well for you as they do for Toyota. Liker stresses that the tools without the right philosophy will not lead to success, warning, "What companies need to be told over and over is that lean tools represent only one aspect of the broader philosophy of the Toyota Way."[3]

In *The Toyota Way*, Liker provides a useful framework for understanding the thinking behind Toyota's success, and the secret behind any successful lean transformation. The key principles are divided into four groups called the 4P's:

1. Philosophy - Base management decisions on long-term philosophy, even at the expense of short-term financial goals.

2. Process - The right process will produce the right result.

3. People and Partners - Add value to the organization by developing your people and partners.

4. Problem Solving - Continuously solving root problems drives organizational learning.

Better Building

While lean thinking and practices have proven successful in every industry, those working in building have a special set of concerns that can make them reluctant to jump on the lean bandwagon. There is something about the temporary nature of project work that steady-state operations like manufacturing don't seem to face. Our work in the building industry is accomplished by temporary teams thrown

---

[3] Jeffrey K. Liker, *The Toyota Way: 14 Management Principles from the World's Greatest Manufacturer* (New York: McGraw-Hill Education, 2004), 297.

together for the purpose of completing a single, unique project. They disband when the project reaches completion, only to do it again on the next project, with an entirely new, unfamiliar team. Some of the specific concerns that we hear most often include the following:

- Our projects are temporary, lasting from just a few months to a couple years. How could we possibly apply a long-term philosophy to our short-term work?

- Our work has so much more variability than manufacturing: weather, indecisive owners, changing priorities, market conditions in each location, variations in workforce, etc. How could we possibly standardize processes and make improvements in the face of such uncertainty?

- Our teams are temporary. How could we possibly create effective teamwork when we don't have the luxury of working together for years like teams at Toyota or other steady-state operations?

- Most of the people who complete our design and construction work aren't even our employees. How could we possibly develop their capabilities and teach them to improve if we may never work with them again after this project?

- Since most workers are not our employees, we have to go through a long, indirect chain of command through subcontractors or suppliers to give any direction. How could we possibly lead a team of people over which we have so little authority?

- Problem solving and continuous improvement are great concepts, but we directly control so little of the process, subcontracting out the majority of the value-added work. How could we possibly make consistent improvements in this environment of custom, one-off projects, and temporary teams?

These are legitimate concerns, and it's easy to see how some people could decide that lean thinking doesn't fit in the project-driven world of building. But it's not as far off as you may think, and there are many examples of lean success in project-driven organizations.

First, recognize that the project-driven organization is not as unique as you might think. Many non-project-driven (steady-state) companies have project-driven organizations within them. When Toyota, a steady-state manufacturer, develops a new car model from concept to production, its product development team is completing project work. A team that invents, designs, and releases new software is also operating in the project-driven world, and has many parallels to the building industry. Likewise, the department that's responsible for building new facilities for a manufacturing, healthcare, or retail company is also a project-driven organization. There are project-driven organizations everywhere that we can learn from, and some of the examples you'll read in this book come from our clients who work as project-driven organizations within broader steady-state companies. The point here is that whether you represent the ownership, design, or construction part of the building process, you are not alone.

I'm going to introduce you to The Better Building model that I devised to be as applicable to a general contractor or trade contractor as it is to an architect, engineer, developer, or project owner. The model is based on our company's many years of experience applying lean thinking to the project-driven world of building, and answers the most common questions that we get asked by those considering a lean transformation for their project or organization. Whatever your place in the project-driven world, the concepts provided here will help you make lean practices work for you, your team, and your organization.

How to Read This Book

The ideas presented here are derived from our work with organizations at every level and in every step of the building process. The book is organized in a way that allows the concepts to build upon each other as you make your way from chapter to chapter. We start at the bottom of The Better Building model with the values and purpose of the organization. From here, I present six core practices that apply specifically to project-driven organizations and help address the unique challenges of this environment.

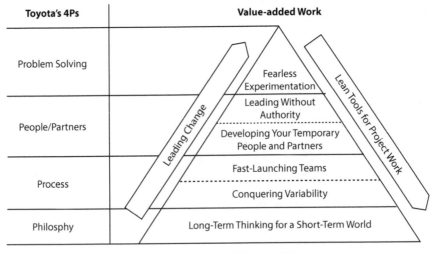

Better Building

The *philosophy*, the first of Toyota's 4Ps, is the foundation for the other practices and is presented in Chapter 1. Chapters 2 and 3 focus on *processes* that can be used to make lean effective in project-driven organizations. Chapters 4 and 5 describe the development of *people and partners*, an especially tricky proposition in project-driven work. Chapter 6 provides insights into learning through experimentation, a concept that correlates with Toyota's fourth P, *problem solving*. As you work your way from one chapter to the next, you will be working your way up the Better Building pyramid, and moving farther from strategy and closer to the value-added work of the company. In a lean organization, providing ever-increasing value to your customer is the ultimate measure of success, and that can only be done through the value-added work. Each practice in the Better Building model supports the ones above it toward accomplishing that overarching goal—increasing value for your customer.

Two additional practices are laid along the sides of the pyramid. On the left side is the "Leading Change" arrow. Applying lean practices in any organization requires effective organizational change as well as the ability to lead that change in your people and partners. The effort originates with the organization's values and purpose, and enables the core practices that lead to the company's value-producing work. The practice of leading change, rather than just managing it, is explained in Chapter 7.

Finally, the practice of applying lean tools specific to the building industry is addressed in Chapter 8. This topic is intentionally left for last, since the tools can only be effective after (or at least in conjunction with) the development of the core lean practices. The arrow emanates from the top of the pyramid, near the value-added work, because tools should serve those who use them, the value creators. In this chapter I provide a brief overview of lean tools that are well-suited to project work and specifically the building industry.

I want to bring your attention to the word *practice*, which appears in the book's subtitle *Lean Practice for the Project-Driven Organization*. It has two meanings here. First, it refers to the application or use of ideas rather than just the theory about their use. Second, it refers to the repeated exercise of a skill to obtain and maintain proficiency in it. The practices described in this book are neither theoretical, like a philosophy, nor tactical, like a tool. Instead, they are a set of skills that can be developed and improved over time to build competency. Just as a doctor practices medicine, or carpenters practice their craft, these competencies must be learned and honed for maximum benefit. After you've finished reading this book, refer back to specific chapters as you *practice* putting specific *practices* into action for yourself.

In alignment with lean thinking, the Better Building model is upside down compared to traditional organizational structure. The front-line workers are at the top and supported from below by the rest of the operation. The entire organization is underpinned by its philosophy, which supports the values and purpose. Whether your organization is a project, company department, or an entire corporation, this structure recognizes that the value-added work must be your primary focus. Building your operation on the practices of the Better Building model will help provide that focus and create alignment at every level.

Before we dig in, let me make two clarifications. First, the term project-driven refers to organizations and teams whose primary function is to complete work on projects. They assemble temporary teams to complete distinct projects as their primary means of serving customers and generating income for their company. All the organizations involved in the process of building are therefore project-driven organizations.

Second, you'll notice that I often refer to *building* or the *building industry* throughout the book. I'm using the term building with a very specific, and maybe unconventional, meaning. Building to me refers to the entire process of inventing, developing, designing, constructing, and occupying our built environment. Whether the project is a highway, airport, hospital, manufacturing plant, refinery, or apartment building, creating it depends on a series of people and organizations each performing their specific part in making it a reality. This distinction is important because the improvements made possible by the Better Building model are not limited to construction alone. In fact, the possibilities for breakthroughs in performance increase when we consider the entire building process.

———

1

Long-Term Thinking for a Short-Term World

THE FOUNDATION OF EVERY organization is its philosophy: how the organization sees itself and the world in which it operates—the organization's way of thinking. Because project-driven organizations' success depends on a string of short-term projects, they tend to put short-term thinking ahead of long-term thinking, thus missing the opportunity to unlock a world of possibilities that don't exist when your primary focus is short-term. This leaves us with two questions. First, why should a company that lives in a short-term project-driven world focus on long-term outcomes and objectives? Second, how can a long-term view be deployed throughout the organization, especially on the projects themselves?

Why Think Long-Term

The foundational concept of prioritizing long-term philosophy over short-term financial goals influences everything that happens at Toyota, and similarly at many other lean companies around the world. Without this long-term perspective, benefits from lean tools and techniques, including profitability, are severely muted, and the full promise of lean thinking can never be achieved. This philosophy has proven successful for more companies than Toyota over the decades. A recent study shows that companies with a long-term mindset significantly outperform their short-term thinking counterparts. The study, which looked at financial results for 615 mid- to large-sized companies from 2001 to 2014, showed 47% higher revenue, 36% higher earnings, and significantly less volatility for companies that managed based on long-term thinking.[4]

To understand the practical implications of this long-term thinking at Toyota, consider a story a client shared with me about his personal experience. Bill had owned a Toyota Sienna minivan for three or four years when he took it to the dealer for routine maintenance. When he dropped off the car, he told the service manager about an annoying rattling sound coming from somewhere beneath the dashboard. The manager agreed to take a look at it and see if they could correct it. He asked if they could keep it overnight in case it took some time to get to the source of the problem.

The next day, Bill picked up his car and the manager was pleased to tell him they found the source of the rattle and eliminated it. The service technicians had actually removed the entire dashboard assembly to find that an anchor clip, which had been incorrectly

---

[4] Dominic Barton, James Manyika, and Sarah Keohane Williamson, "Finally, Evidence That Managing for the Long Term Pays Off," *Harvard Business Review*, February 9, 2017, https://hbr.org/2017/02/finally-proof-that-managing-for-the-long-term-pays-off.

installed in the factory, had vibrated loose over time. Bill was surprised when the manager offered his sincere apology that the part had been installed incorrectly and for the inconvenience. Although the warranty for this type of issue had long expired, the dealer did not charge him for the repair. Bill was impressed and pleased with the outcome.

Just one week later, Bill got another surprise in the mail. He received a letter from the manager of the automotive interiors department at the factory where his Sienna had been assembled several years earlier. The manager apologized again for the assembly error and offered Bill a small discount on a future Toyota purchase. The letter also thanked Bill for bringing the issue to Toyota's attention and included a description of the changes they made to the assembly procedure to ensure the problem would not happen again. Bill told me (and probably dozens of others) that he had become a Toyota customer for life.

This example of doing what is right for the customer, even when it doesn't have an immediate financial payback, demonstrates Toyota's incorporation of long-term thinking into its foundational philosophy, and that it's applied consistently at all levels of the organization.

In his book *Good to Great*, Jim Collins describes the long-term philosophy he found in companies that consistently outperform their industry peers. He equates the long-term thinking of great companies with a massive flywheel.[5] His research showed that companies who initiate dramatic change programs or drastic restructurings almost always fail to become great companies. The most successful companies achieved their success through steadily working toward consistent goals over long periods of time. Like a team of people pushing on a giant flywheel, building momentum turn after turn, companies build energy and power through the accumulation of small, consistent efforts every day.

---

[5] Jim Collins, *Good to Great: Why Some Companies Make the Leap and Others Don't* (New York: HarperBusiness, 2001), 14.

Both Liker and Collins discovered a similar truth about organizations that flies in the face of much of today's conventional corporate behavior, which rewards leaders for short-term successes, quick wins, and hitting quarterly numbers. They discovered that great companies think first about the long-term implications of their actions before worrying about short-term results. Perhaps not surprisingly, the long-term focused companies have consistently better short-term results, higher returns, and faster growth than their short-term focused peers.

A Tale of Two Developers

Over the years, I've had the opportunity to complete building projects for a variety of commercial real estate developers. They all fit the definition of project-driven organizations to a tee; their primary business is to create buildings for their clients, one unique project at a time. For each project, they bring together a temporary team, which always includes engineers, architects, financing resources, and constructors. Often, they include specialists to help deal with logistics, traffic and transportation, environmental remediation, regional market research, and any number of regulatory and financial issues.

Unlike speculative real estate deals, each project was done to meet the needs of one specific client, and the developer's profit came primarily from the fees the client paid. I recall working on many types of building projects including factories, hotels, medical office buildings, parking ramps, distribution centers, dormitories, warehouses, retail stores, and even a couple of breweries.

In my years working with these developers, there were two very successful companies that exemplify the difference between long-term and short-term thinking. I'll refer to them as LT Development and ST Real Estate Company.

ST Real Estate Company (STREAC) was a company that had been successful in the regional market for years. They were profitable and well-respected locally. They donated money to community non-profits, and were well connected to the local political power structure. Their success was the result of a business philosophy that was embodied in a mantra that I heard the owner repeat many times: "We never lose money on a project!"

This feat is easier to say than it is to achieve. Commercial real estate development is a risk-filled business. Between shifting owner needs, unknown site conditions, hard-to-predict construction costs, and an ever-changing financial environment, much can go wrong during the three-to-five-year lifecycle of a typical development project. I've seen many projects fail on the drawing board, and I've seen multiple development companies go bankrupt when one project goes bad. ST Real Estate was a solid company that knew how to manage these risks.

This mindset, or philosophy, of keeping every project profitable at all cost is a classic short-term thinking approach, and many project-driven companies subscribe to the thinking. What it meant in practice at STREAC was that the most important measure of success was the profitability of each project, and everyone in the company knew it.

I worked on only one project with STREAC, and my company was the third general contractor to be engaged on the project. The first general contractor worked for a year on pricing and actually broke ground on the project while the budget was still being finalized—a common practice in fast-track projects. Before the concrete foundations were complete, it became clear that they would not be able to construct the building within budget. In response, STREAC decided to take the project out for bid. This was mainly an attempt to get their contractor to "sharpen their pencils," but in the end, it was a small, inexperienced out-of-town contractor that delivered the low bid; the only bid that actually met the project's budget.

Contractor #2 worked for several months erecting the structure and getting the building weathertight. To win the project, which could have opened up a new market segment for the company, they had taken a big risk with their low bid, and immediately took a defensive approach to their relationship with STREAC. The contractor submitted multiple claims for delays and extra costs, threatening to stop work on the project if the developer did not agree to the extras. In response, STREAC filed counterclaims against the contractor alleging that their poor management and pricing errors were the cause of delays and cost overruns. The developer eventually removed the contractor from the project amid a storm of legal action that would not be resolved until two years after the project was complete.

STREAC finally hired my company, contractor #3, to complete the work on the building on a time and materials basis. We knew STREAC's reputation as a tough and litigious company, so we made sure that contractually, we took no responsibility for budgets or schedules; there was just too much baggage from the earlier parts of the project to be confident that we could untangle the mess and keep ourselves clear of the risk.

In the end, the project finished on time, although the last two months were a whirlwind of costly overtime, expedited deliveries, and double-shift work in the field. The owner was able to move in on time, but there were multiple quality issues that took months to resolve while the building was in service. There was an issue with condensation inside the building windows—an ongoing dispute between STREAC, the architect, and the contractor that I don't think was ever resolved. The owner just learned to live with it.

STREAC settled a lawsuit with contractor #1 about six months after completion. The lawsuit with contractor #2 went on for almost two years. The company, which was really too small and inexperienced for a project of this size, went out of business waiting for payment during the final settlement negotiations. Many of their subcontractors and suppliers, who had been waiting for years to get paid themselves, settled for pennies on the dollar through the bankruptcy process.

STREAC would not claim that this was their best project, but they did make a small profit after settlements and legal fees. Other, more profitable projects would keep their financial position strong, and new projects were always in the works. The trail of disputes and unhappy project participants was not unusual for a STREAC project. They knew that they could always find new "partners" by looking outside the regional market or tapping a smaller contractor with an alluring opportunity to step up to a larger project. There were always companies willing to take the risk, despite STREAC's reputation.

STREAC's clients were mostly one-time builders; companies that might only need development services once or twice in a generation. This could be a manufacturer that was building a new factory, an auto dealership building its first new store in twenty years, or a business that needed a new office building. STREAC offered these companies a local, well-connected, affordable source for their projects, and there were always plenty of opportunities to keep STREAC's backlog full.

LT Development (LTD), although they worked in the same market and had a similar financial model, had a contrasting perspective on project work. My company built dozens of projects for LTD, and we were one of only three or four contractors that LTD used in the region. They were a demanding company to work for, with high expectations for performance, and they provided us a steady workload. Other contractors were always knocking on their door, but LTD was selective, and getting a shot at one of their projects came only to those with years of demonstrated ability and a reputation for a collaborative company culture. LTD was looking for relationships, not one-off deals.

LTD approached their clients the same way, and most were frequent builders: a healthcare company that operated three dozen clinics in the region, a growing auto dealership that owned fifteen locations, and a specialty retailer that had forty stores throughout the Midwest. They appreciated LTD's open, collaborative approach, and had grown to trust them for their real estate needs. As each company expanded geographically, LTD went with them, and often brought their construction partners along as well.

I remember a project with a particularly short time frame, where the construction schedule was threatened by incomplete design information, primarily because the owner was unable to make decisions about the building aesthetics. The retail chain was actually going through a rebranding, and this building was stuck between the old and new look for the façade and interiors. In addition, the customer flow was being reconsidered, and the entire layout of the building was in flux. While the owner and architect wrestled with store layouts, window systems, and interior finish selections, the construction schedule began to slip, threatening the on-time opening of the building. In another environment, this could have easily deteriorated into a series of notices and claims, as each party defended itself against the risk of cost overruns and schedule delays. The result on this project was quite different.

Instead, LTD convened an emergency design session. The idea was to determine what could be done within the given timeframe, and plan a path forward together. Over the two-day meeting, attended by my company, LTD, the owner, architect, and several key trade contractors and suppliers, we developed a plan that satisfied the updated needs of the project.

The building layout, which impacted things like location of columns and underslab plumbing, would remain unchanged. These elements were already under construction and would be very expensive and disruptive to modify. The exterior building systems, which had the longest lead times and had to be ordered soon, would stay with the current materials as well, although they would be modified slightly to allow exterior elements like signage and awnings to be easily changed later. The interiors, which included casework, flooring, ceilings, and everything else that customers would see inside the building, would be switched to the new branding look at minimal cost and with no schedule impact. The result was a store that, although it didn't completely incorporate the new branding scheme, would not require a major renovation after it opened.

To accomplish this plan, many suppliers and contractors found a way to expedite materials and installation at little or no cost to the project. It was an extraordinary effort, but they had the best interests of the owner in mind, and worked hard to meet the new project objectives. When the electrical contractor confessed that he could not provide the manpower to get the electrical changes done in time, we agreed to supplement his crew with workers from another contractor. The electrician lost out on some potential profit, but maintained his reputation with this team, and was certain to be considered for future projects. The designers and owner were flexible and used the input of the project team to immediately understand which elements could be changed and which could not. The project was delivered within its original budget and opened smoothly, right on time.

The teamwork, collaboration, and trust of the group were leveraged to solve a tough problem in a way that would be impossible in a short-term thinking environment. While LTD did not create this environment single-handedly, it was their long-term philosophy that made it possible. The culture on their projects was founded in their approach: how they select clients, partners, and suppliers, how they dealt with problems, and how they worked together in the best interest of their clients. LTD did not create this environment overnight. They built it over time, continually pushing the flywheel in the same direction, building momentum and energy, one project after the other.

Although philosophy is somewhat ethereal, the contrasting stories of STREAC and LTD show how a company's way of thinking becomes evident in the choices it makes over time. These choices, guided by the underlying philosophy, affect every part of a business, and ultimately determine the strategic direction of the organization. While STREAC's growth was limited by its short-term thinking, the long-term philosophy of LTD let them develop a nationwide real estate business focused on serving the growing needs of their repeat customers.

The following table lists opposing approaches to various business issues that exemplify both the short- and long-term perspectives in project-driven organizations. I'm sure you'll recognize both in your own market.

	Short-Term Thinking	**Long-Term Thinking**
Employee Development	Training is expensive – teach your people only enough to do their jobs on this project.	Train your people to become flexible resources who continuously solve problems and make improvements from project to project
Vendor Selection	Select the low bidder and make sure they know the competition is always on their heels.	Help partners improve their processes. Develop them to become valuable long-term partners, improving from one project to the next.
Customer Relationships	Maximize profit on every project.	Do the right thing for the customer, even when they aren't looking.
Compensation	Pay employees for piecework to minimize cost and get as much from each person as you can.	Pay a salary and a bonus for company performance based on customer value.
Quality Control	Inspectors find problems before the project is delivered to the customer. Use punch lists and specialists to make repairs.	Stop the work to fix problems as they are found so quality is built-in. Take the time to do it right the first time.

	Short-Term Thinking	**Long-Term Thinking**
Decision-Making	Make decisions as quickly as possible to stay ahead of project timelines.	Make decisions slowly by consensus at the last responsible moment, allowing maximum flexibility and ensuring decisions are not second-guessed later in the project.
Growth	Grow quickly through acquisitions, even at the expense of company culture.	Steady, organic growth that focuses on building capabilities and maintaining the culture.
Cost Control	Slash costs any way possible to hit estimates – profitability is the highest measure of success.	Make improvements continuously to achieve ever higher productivity and improved customer value over time.
Improvement	Hire outside experts to make big changes to operations whenever the company is struggling.	Require everyone to make incremental improvements all the time. Build learning into the culture of the company and its partners.
Risk	Push risks downstream through contracting strategies and tighten contract language.	Work collaboratively with project partners to eliminate or reduce risks rather than just move them to others.
Contract Structure	Use transactional contracts to define minimal project requirements and create a basis for litigation if necessary.	Use relational contracts to define how partners will behave together to meet project objectives collaboratively.
Outsourcing	Replace internal capabilities with external resources to increase profit. Use subcontractors any time they provide a lower price.	Develop skills and capabilities within the company, which will serve to provide long-term flexibility and opportunity for growth over time.

Understanding the impact of long-term thinking is only half the battle. A philosophy, no matter how powerful, is only effective when it is put into strategic action at all levels of the organization, much like we saw Toyota do with Bill's Sienna. But how does a company instill its philosophy into every person, at every level, not to mention into its partners and suppliers? Lean companies have figured it out, and with just a little modification, it can be applied to any project-driven organization.

Deploy Strategy to the Project Level

Studies have shown that almost six out of ten strategic initiatives fail to have any positive impact on the company after one year.[6] Given the energy and expense that companies spend on strategic initiatives, it is no wonder that individuals often feel burned out and uninspired by the latest initiative that rolls down from leadership. Many times, I've witnessed management's announcement of a new initiative being met with eye-rolls and sighs from the people in the organization. They have been here before and learned that strategic initiatives mean more training and reporting for them, while offering no real improvement in their project outcomes.

Lean companies, on the other hand, have built in a process for creating effective strategy and engaging people at all levels to apply it. The strategy becomes a force to drive the organization forward while, at the same time, benefiting every manager and worker, from bottom to top. When the organization is fully aligned around the strategy, it moves forward as one powerful unit. In Collins' terms, the entire organization is pushing the flywheel in the same direction, and

---

[6] "Why Good Strategies Fail: Lessons for the C-Suite," *The Economist Intelligence Unit Limited*, 2013, https://www.pmi.org/-/media/pmi/documents/public/pdf/learning/thought-leadership/why-good-strategies-fail-report.pdf.

is benefitting from the momentum and energy the flywheel provides in return.

This lean strategy deployment approach, called Hoshin Kanri, evolved with lean manufacturing concepts in Japan decades ago. The term translates to "direction management," with Hoshin meaning compass or direction, and Kanri meaning administration. The process is straightforward, but requires practice to implement effectively. In addition, the unique circumstances of the project-driven environment require some slight adjustments to the approach used in manufacturing firms.

Lean Strategy Deployment

Value-added Work

Strategic Goals (upward arrow) • **Results** (downward arrow)

| Project-Level Targets |
| Tactical Objectives |
| Operational Goals |
| Strategic Initiatives |

Values and Purpose

Lean strategy deployment for project-driven organizations starts with annual strategic objectives that leadership develops in alignment with long-term goals and organizational philosophy. The objectives are focused and limited in number, usually not more than two or three objectives in a given year. We've worked with companies that have tried to implement a dozen initiatives at once, and have seen how this lack of focus results in the achievement of none. When we challenge our clients to narrow the list of annual initiatives by focusing on their long-term philosophy, it results in more impactful strategy and a greater likelihood of success. Each time an initiative gets dropped from the list of possible options, the remaining options become more powerful. This refinement of initiatives requires the leadership team to determine what is truly important and provides the focus needed to meet the company's long-term goals.

Once the strategic initiatives are established for a given year, the leadership is ready to deploy them through the organization. Organization leaders present the initiatives to the next level in a catchball process, where they negotiate specific implementation steps and establish measurable goals. Imagine a game of hot potato where a senior manager hands a set of objectives to a department leader and requests a detailed plan to meet the objectives. The leader replies quickly with a plan, which includes implementation steps and metrics, and passes it back to the manager. The manager critiques the plan and challenges the department head to improve it. Whatever the case, the potato is tossed back and forth between the two in quick cycles until they reach a common understanding, and the leader commits to a plan. The process then repeats between the department leader and the next level of leaders until the strategic objectives are distilled to every level of the organization. In project-driven organizations, this means deploying the strategy to the projects themselves. The concept is shown in the illustration that follows.

Catchball Process

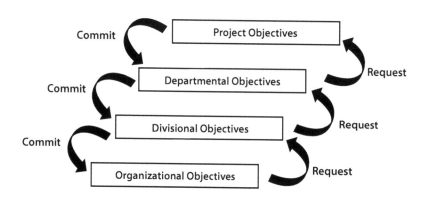

This negotiation allows leadership to set the strategy while the operational level is allowed (and required) to determine the tactical steps that they will use to achieve the required results. The process is iterative and requires each layer of the organization to gain a full understanding of the strategic initiatives and how they align with the company's long-term philosophy. It's an ongoing process of education, feedback, coaching, and accountability.

This translation of strategy to tactical objectives happens at each successive layer of the organization in preparation for deploying the strategy to the projects themselves. In most project-driven organizations, there are just one or two steps from top leadership to divisional or regional operating units. The process is intense and occurs within a time frame of just a couple weeks. Once the operating units have established their plans for executing the strategy, including a process for measuring and reporting results throughout the year, they are prepared to deploy it on the projects.

The nature of project work means that each project does not necessarily fit nicely into a one-year time frame. Many projects are already underway when an initiative is established, and other projects are not yet started, and will have little opportunity to deliver results in the coming twelve months. This issue of aligning project time frames with annual strategic initiatives is the biggest barrier to applying strategy to the actual work in project-driven organizations. As a result, many organizations stop strategic initiatives at the operating group level and never actually deploy them to their actual work, the projects themselves.

Since, in a project-driven organization, it is the project level where the company interfaces with its customers, suppliers, and partners, it is essential that the strategy be deployed at this primary level. Stopping strategy deployment at the operating group level is like playing football from the sidelines. You are too far removed from the action for the strategy to have any significant impact on the value-added work of the projects.

When we help companies with strategy deployment, we insist that every initiative must, with rare exception, be implemented on every project. This is accomplished through the same catchball negotiation that brought the initiative from leadership to the operating group level. The group manager challenges each project team with a specific objective, and the project team makes a proposal for how it will be accomplished. This back and forth process continues until the project team and manager are in agreement about the specific plan and the outcomes that should be achieved on that project. Since each project will be at a different stage of completion during this process, each will have its own unique set of goals.

One of our clients established a strategic initiative to employ the Last Planner® System[7] (LPS) as their new process for planning and executing construction on at least half of its projects within twelve months. This corporate-level initiative cascaded to all operating units,

[7] Last Planner® System, now a common lean practice in design and construction, is a registered trademark of Lean Construction Institute. More details of its use are provided in Chapter 8.

where it was translated into specific goals for each unit. In one region, the manager set the goal of applying LPS to every project in his unit. For that region, the plan included providing some level of LPS training to every superintendent and project manager. It also included training internal coaches and LPS experts who could support its use on projects. Developing these folks eventually eliminated the need for us, an outside consultant, to do LPS training and coaching. This was a powerful example of deploying strategy to the operating unit level, but the real impact happened on the projects.

The regional manager met with each project team to determine how far they could go with LPS on their specific project. For one healthcare project, which had almost completed construction, the team proposed to use LPS to coordinate and manage the owner move-in process. This was a very limited scope for LPS, but since the construction was virtually complete, it was appropriate for the project. The move-in went well, and the owner said the transition was the smoothest he'd ever experienced.

On another project, which had just broken ground, the team decided to use the project as an LPS training ground for their superintendents, foremen, project managers, and trade partners. We conducted intensive training of lean concepts (including LPS) for the entire project team, and coached team leaders in the behaviors and practices that were needed for LPS to be successful. It was an intensive effort that required a big investment, but was well worth it for a large twenty-month project, which achieved a level of coordination, workflow, and productivity that surprised everyone. The implementation of LPS and coaching that took place made the project a regular "field trip" destination for others who were learning to use LPS. The project team opened the doors to anyone who wanted to learn. This included employees from other projects and regions, trade contractors who may or may not have been engaged on the project, and even competitors who were considering a switch to LPS themselves. The LPS success on that one project fueled confidence and enthusiasm for lean throughout the entire company.

If you think this approach to lean strategy deployment seems intense, serious, and challenging, you're right. It is not a superficial two-week exercise that quickly fades into the background and becomes swallowed up by the daily priorities that drive a project-driven organization. Instead, it integrates strategy into the work of the entire organization, making improvements as part of the daily operations, not as an afterthought or side job. The work is hard, but extremely rewarding. The effort pays back in so many ways for a lean organization:

- Strategic initiatives succeed and drive the progress of the organization.

- Everyone in the company understands and lives the philosophy and culture.

- Individuals at all levels develop leadership and management skills.

- Project teams learn to work together to make improvements.

- The company learns what it is capable of and sets increasingly challenging goals.

Just as described by both Liker and Collins, the ability for a company to act on its long-term philosophy becomes a strategic advantage, helping it deliver more value for its customers and outperform its peers. Developing this capability in your project-driven organization is essential for continuous improvement, and creates the foundation upon which the organization's lean practices can thrive.

————

2

Conquering Variability

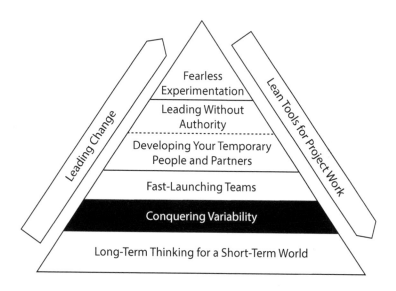

I'M OFTEN ASKED TO introduce lean concepts to groups that work in project environments—mostly in the building industry. Typical audience members include construction executives, project managers, superintendents and foremen, architects, design engineers, and people who represent project owners of companies that are constantly building new facilities like hospitals and factories. Collectively, they are building industry veterans who have a lifetime of experience in every aspect of project work.

I start this introduction to lean by explaining that lean was originally developed in the manufacturing environment, and has since been successfully applied to many other industries. To help convey lean's potential, I'll often share stories and statistics from organizations that have had success by changing from traditional to lean ways of thinking and managing their work. Without making major investments in new equipment or additional staff, here are some of the results that have been reported across various industries:[8]

- Annual lost workdays at an aluminum casting plant reduced from 1.9 to 0.1 per 200,000 hours worked.

- Recordable injuries reduced from 6.9 to 1.1 per 200,000 hours worked.

- Jet engine development costs reduced from $1 billion to $300 million.

- Development time reduced from four years to two and a half.

- Productivity at a mattress manufacturer doubled while finished goods inventory shrunk from 30 to 1.5 days.

- A flu shot clinic went from administering six shots per hour to thirty shots per hour while reducing staff.

- Hospital-acquired infections for patients receiving a central line decreased from thirty-seven to three while the number of central lines increased by 64%.

- Annual infection-related deaths decreased from nineteen to zero.

- Average patient waiting time (in hospital gowns in public waiting rooms) reduced from twenty-five minutes to zero.

As people from the project-driven world learn about these types of results from lean, their reaction usually comes in two parts. First, they are surprised how impactful lean has been, and that it has been

[8] Steven J. Spear, *The High-Velocity Edge: How Market Leaders Leverage Operational Excellence to Beat the Competition* (New York: McGraw Hill, 2009), 89,144,183, 330, 340, 344.

applied to so many different industries. Although there is some healthy skepticism, like wondering how bad these sample operations must have been before lean came along, most people are energized to think that big improvements are possible.

The second part of the response usually sounds something like this: "These results are great, but this stuff could never work in construction. There is just too much uncertainty and change." I've worked in the construction industry for almost thirty years and I know that it's much different from the assembly line process for making widgets, or even Toyota Camrys. I understand their skepticism!

It's true that the project-driven world of the building industry has many types of variability that most manufacturing operations do not have to deal with. First, there are the environmental issues related to this type of work, like weather and unforeseen site conditions. An assembly worker in a Toyota plant has never opened a wall to make a plumbing tie-in only to discover that the existing pipes are wrapped in asbestos—the type of revelation that happens daily on construction projects and can completely disrupt the flow of work.

The temporary nature of project teams is another challenge—an architect who is working with an owner for the first (and possibly only) time, a subcontractor who is new to a certain geographic area, and a worker who is teamed with a group of people he has never met before. In this environment, participants are usually employed by many different companies, often with competing interests. Getting everyone to work as a cohesive team is not automatic, and sometimes it's not even in their own best interest. They might be financially better off to focus on their own productivity at the expense of project outcomes.

Project work, by its nature, is also less repetitive and predictable. Most projects are a one-time effort—we almost never design and build the same project twice. Even when projects are repetitive, like the construction of similar retail stores or medical clinics in multiple locations, there are always variations in design due to local soil conditions, building codes, and material preferences. In addition, the experience of the suppliers and workforce is unique to each location. Designers and builders often struggle when they try to apply processes from one location to another, even when it is in a neighboring town.

While I agree that variation and change are an inherent part of project work, and that this is more prevalent in the building industry than in manufacturing, I do not agree that lean cannot work here. In fact, we have helped many projects and companies get dramatic results using lean practices, and it is the best approach that I know of to deal with the variability of our project-driven world.

To put lean to work in the uncertain world of project-driven work, we break the solution down into two components. First, minimize variation to maximize workflow. Second, design your work processes to accommodate the variability that cannot be eliminated. I'll explain how to do both of these for powerful results.

Minimize Variation to Maximize Workflow

Our method for minimizing variation can be described in four steps as shown in the illustration. First, since variation can be hard to see in project work, we make it visible by measuring it and displaying it publicly for the project team. Next, we work to eliminate the variation that is within our control, putting our own house in order first. A colleague once called these issues the "slow, fat rabbits" of continuous improvement—easy targets to pick off that can pay big dividends. These steps will help build your team's confidence and begin to expand your circle of influence[9] beyond your immediate project team, giving you the ability to influence people and processes that you previously could not. Finally, we use our new, larger circle of influence to uncover and reduce

---

[9] Stephen R. Covey, *The 7 Habits of Highly Effective People* (New York: Simon & Schuster, 1989). The Circle of Influence concept comes from this book.

variation further up the value chain, repeating the cycle as an ongoing process for minimizing variation. This four-step approach has helped our clients reduce many sources of variation that they once thought were untouchable.

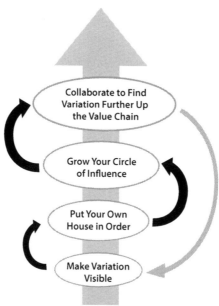

Several years ago we were hired by a global microchip producer—I'll call them MicroMax Technologies—to help improve the speed, cost, and reliability of getting their latest chip offerings to market. This meant improving the process they used to design and build new chip plants. These are multi-billion dollar projects that utilize a construction workforce of up to four thousand tradespeople to build complex facilities and install the tools that actually produce microchips. I had never worked in a chip plant before, and I was amazed at both the scale and complexity of the process.

We were supporting a "tool-install" project, where hundreds of chip-producing tools had to be installed in a time frame of less than twelve months. The term "tool" is used in the microchip industry to describe a piece of equipment that has some role in manufacturing microchips. Some tools are multi-million dollar pieces of robotic equipment, which perform one step on the chips, like printing a layer of microscopic circuitry or adding an insulating layer between circuits. Other tools are much simpler, like filters or pumps that treat the chemicals going in and out of the manufacturing process. Many tools were located on the cleanroom (or fab) floor, which required an ultra-clean environment to prevent microscopic particles or fluctuating environmental conditions from ruining the chips. Other tools were positioned one floor below the cleanroom in the sub-fab. Each tool had a myriad of inputs and outputs that had to be connected to each other and to the infrastructure of the overall plant. This could include dozens of specialty (and often deadly) chemicals, electrical and control connections, lasers, etching acids, ultrapure water, and gases. A single tool may have two dozen piping connections ranging in size from 1/8 inch to 8 inches. It could also have a half dozen different waste outlets that need to be connected to various treatment and processing systems within the plant.

There was a lot of variety in the amount of work required to install any given tool. A very complex tool could have a construction duration of up to fifty working days, while the simplest tools may only take a couple days to install.

Picture the cleanroom tools as a series of minivans parked about twenty feet apart, with each one hooked to more lines and controls than are used to operate most buildings in their entirety. Each one is connected to a series of simpler tools: controllers, pumps, filters, and other process equipment in the sub-fab, one floor below. If you look up when standing in the sub-fab, you'll see a maze of conduits and pipes that starts just above your head and continues to the floor above at a height of nearly twenty feet. This maze of complexity continues for acres and acres in a single chip plant.

On this particular project, we were working to bring some stability to the design and construction process, to eliminate problems with late delivery of tools, and reduce the very high costs of overtime and rework. The company's inability to deliver individual tools on time and on budget, compounded over several hundred tools, threatened the ability of MicroMax to deliver its latest chip technology to the market on time. Missing key delivery dates of the latest chip technology for clients like Apple, Microsoft, and IBM could obviously be catastrophic.

In a large meeting with the project team, which included MicroMax construction project managers, third party piping and electrical designers, representatives from a dozen trade contractors, and the construction manager, we wanted to get to the heart of one issue: the flow of work was so erratic and unpredictable that no single worker could consistently accomplish everything they needed to on any given day. The project had degraded into a firefighting mindset—responding quickly to the crisis of the moment, at the expense of important project milestones and delivery dates.

Our question for the project team: What was the cause of so much churn on the project, and was there anything we could do about it?

The first comments came from the MicroMax project managers. "In our industry, we must be responsive to the needs of our customers and the process for developing this cutting-edge technology. When our customer needs a change in the chip design, or our technology development engineers need to tweak a fabrication sequence, our construction must respond immediately. It's just the nature of our business." These views were quickly echoed by some MicroMax technology development leaders.

The engineers and designers also chimed in, "We must respond quickly to any changes from MicroMax so it can achieve its goals. As a result, we cannot make reliable commitments to complete design work for any individual tool. Our priorities change daily."

The contractors added, "We've tried for years to develop clear, stable plans for completing construction at this site. It's futile in this environment, and we're much better off just doing our best to be responsive each day." The construction manager agreed, "We were hired because we can be responsive to the change that Micromax demands." Although everyone in the room realized that this constant firefighting was a very expensive and unreliable way to get work done, their comments were a chorus for acceptance of the status quo.

Only a few among the group, mainly the MicroMax executives, understood that this way of doing business was not sustainable in a microchip industry that had become more competitive and needed to move faster than ever before. The team's stuck-in-a-rut perception of how work should get done, and its inability to improve the stability of the design and construction process could kill their company.

At the insistence of MicroMax executives, and with plenty of skepticism, the team members reluctantly agreed to take a first step in an experiment to see if there was anything to be done about the variability and uncertainty in their processes. They agreed to measure the amount of variability that came into the construction process on a weekly basis; the first step in conquering variability. They measured the "churn," defined as the percentage of construction activities that were subject to a change within six weeks of starting the work. They also agreed to publicly plot the churn on a chart in the large room where most of the project meetings were held.

After a couple weeks, the first churn data became available. We found that about 60 percent of construction activities experienced a change within six weeks prior to starting the work. This could mean the reroute of a piping line, change in electrical or control systems, moving the tool to a different location in the plant, or even removing a tool from the worklist in favor of another, higher-priority tool. No one was surprised by the data, and for many, the data confirmed their perception that this is how work gets done on a MicroMax project. Whatever their perception, the variability was now visible to the team.

Once we had a good way to measure the variability, or churn, of the project, we were surprised to see that it actually started to fall a bit. We suspected this was because people were starting to pay attention to the problem, but we weren't sure until we took the next step.

After two weeks, we asked for another experiment—this one to test our ability to reduce at least some of the variation. For each change that was made, which was already heavily documented to justify overtime spending or schedule adjustments, the team would identify the person originating the change and the reason for it. Maybe if we understood why the change was happening, we could get to the root cause and make some improvements. This was the start of step two—putting our own house in order. The results were surprising.

After measuring the churn for only a couple more weeks, and recording the origin and reason for each change, the amount of churn began to decrease—significantly. In fact, over just three weeks, the churn on the project shrank from 60 to 20 percent! This result, which seemed impossible only a few weeks earlier, came without changing project leadership or making any major policy changes. It seemed that just measuring the churn and making the information public were causing it to shrink. The churn trend for the project, as shown in the chart, was beginning to show results.

I talked with several MicroMax project managers to better understand what was happening. What was allowing such a dramatic reduction in churn? While no single change in behavior explained the entire decrease, the confession of one project manager gave me a pretty strong indication. He explained that MicroMax measured performance by the ability to complete a certain number of tools through construction each week. Based on the number of tools and the time frame for this specific project, each PM was expected to complete something like six tools per week. If each of the PMs achieved this goal, the thinking was, the project would generally remain on track.

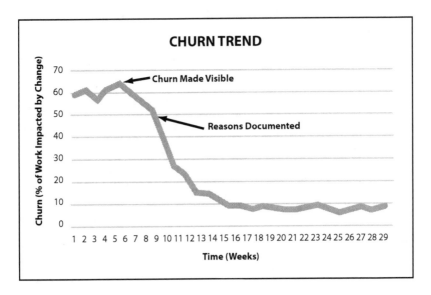

This individual performance metric was serious business for MicroMax project managers. It was a key piece of information used during salary reviews, and a strong consideration when it came time for promotions or layoffs. Each project manager knew that they had to achieve a high weekly tool completion rate if they wanted to be successful at MicroMax. After private conversations with several PMs, I discovered that this performance metric was inadvertently contributing to the churn of the project.

If a project manager was responsible for a very complex tool that was supposed to be complete the following week, they did whatever they could to make sure the tool was actually completed. That meant they would shift resources from other tools, and even ignore their own responsibility for other tools, to make sure the "priority tool" got done in time. This resulted in wild variations in the workflow and the attention that was given to individual tools from one week to the next. While this practice was pervasive across the project and created great churn for the construction team, it was not the biggest surprise I found.

If the same project manager realized that this complex high-priority tool would in fact not finish the next week as required to make their numbers, they had to go to plan B. This meant that they would look for a very simple tool, one that was not yet scheduled for work, but had all the necessary design information and materials available on site. Although this simple tool was not needed for many weeks, the project manager would move it up in the schedule and make it a high-priority tool. This meant that the contractors would drop everything in order to get it installed as quickly as possible. A simple tool that could be installed in just a few days helped the project manager meet their delivery goals for the week.

Many project managers used this practice to quietly meet their delivery numbers while adding no value to the project; adding instead to the disruption, uncertainty, and inability of the construction team to achieve any kind of flow in their work. We had found at least one of the root causes of churn in the project, and it was an issue that was primarily within the control of the project team.

With this kind of early, positive result, the team became energized, and their circle of influence grew beyond the traditional limits of their project. They began to engage with MicroMax technology developers and others further up the supply chain to measure and attack more causes of variation and uncertainty. They uncovered one cause after another and implemented simple changes to eliminate, or at least reduce, the impact on construction activities. Within six weeks, they were able to reduce the churn to near 5 percent, where it stayed for the remainder of the project. The uncontrolled variability—one of the biggest barriers to project success and a problem that everyone was certain could not be improved— was almost eliminated in just a few weeks.

This story illustrates the first part of conquering variability on project work—eliminate as much as you can to allow the work to flow. In this example and in other similar situations, we accomplish this by following the four steps outlined earlier. First, measure the variability and make it visible. This step alone often has amazing results. Then, put your own house in order by addressing the root causes that are within your immediate control. This process increases the team's confidence and the influence it has over others in the value stream. Finally, we use this new influence to work collaboratively to find and eliminate more causes of variation and bring increasing stability to the project. The cycle repeats, finding variation and reducing it further and further up the value stream over time. The lesson for those working in the project environment is that there is almost always something you can do about variability—much more that you might think.

Design Work Processes to Accommodate Variability That Remains

As this process for minimizing variation is continuously repeated and driven further up the value chain, more and more variation will be driven out of the workflow. However, not all variation can be eliminated. Unexpected and unpredictable events that get in the way of reliably completing work on projects are always part of the process. Additionally, some types of variability are actually required to provide flexibility and responsiveness to the changing needs of the customer. This flexibility adds value for the project owner, and we must be careful not to eliminate variation at the expense of flexibility. Whether the variability that remains is left intentionally, or as a potential target for future reduction, the project team must have a way to manage it to minimize its impact on the flow of work.

We have at our disposal many lean techniques that can help manage variability, and some are better suited to the project environment than others. We've found that on most projects, there are three approaches that can make a big difference: planning and executing work in small batches, using visible buffers that are shared by the team, and making decisions and plans at the last responsible moment. Let's take them one at a time.

Plan and Execute Work in Small Batches

In the manufacturing environment, it's easy to see how work flows through a process in batches. A worker completes ten assemblies at their station and loads them on a pallet, which is transported to the next station where another worker completes the next operation on the same ten assemblies. This batch of ten may work its way through the entire plant until it reaches completion and is shipped off to the customer, also in a batch. The flow is a physical movement of the work through the system; you could actually see the entire process flow by walking a single batch through the plant.

The problems with working in large batches are that it takes a long time to get one piece of work through the entire process and it requires a lot of inventory in the system, which in turn hides any problems in the process. A defect created in one assembly station might not be discovered until the entire batch of ten makes it through the next station, or possibly to the end of the entire process. This dramatically slows the time it takes to correct problems and make improvements.

When manufacturers apply lean thinking, they work to reduce the size of batches, ultimately striving for single piece flow as a way of improving the outcomes of the process. Working in smaller batches reduces the amount of inventory (or buffers) in the system, and makes problems visible very quickly. Since assemblies flow through the plant as single units, it also shortens the time to delivery, increases productivity, lowers costs, and provides more flexibility to make changes. If the customer suddenly needs a different mix of parts, or if there is a sudden spike in the demand for red Camrys, the small-batch manufacturer can respond much faster than one who has mountains of inventory that must first be cleared through the system. If you're not familiar with the concept of small batches and single piece flow, check out the examples in *This is Lean* by Niklas Modig. The small batch approach has been around for decades and is a proven technique for increasing speed and adding flexibility in manufacturing and many other industries.

In project work, it's difficult to see the batches, let alone think about making them smaller. A carpenter hanging drywall in the rooms of a hotel project does not put their completed work on a pallet and send it to the painter to do the next step. Builders typically think of their work as a continuous stream without clear starting and stopping points. They work their way through the project, room by room and floor to floor, until all their work is completed. Multiple operations overlap each other, and it can be very difficult to visualize the flow of work or size of a batch. Project-driven organizations rarely plan or execute their work in batches, and when they do, the batches are large, like the entire floor of a building. We often see the same large-batch thinking in design work. An architect knows that the plans must be ready for submittal to the city in five months. Although the work passes through the hands of many different designers, they rarely divide the project into small batches to improve the flow.

When we explain the idea of small batches to clients, we use this simple diagram to illustrate how this approach increases speed of work flowing through the system. In the first diagram, five trades work their way through this five-story building in large batches—one floor at time. As each trade completes their work on one batch, they

---

[10] Niklas Modig and Pär Åhlström, *This is Lean* (Stockholm: Rheologica Publishing, 2013).

move on to the next, with subsequent trades following just one batch behind them. When the drywaller is beginning work on the fifth floor, the casework installer is just getting started on the first floor. If each trade takes five days to complete a floor, the project will take forty-five days to complete.

Batch Size = 1 Floor

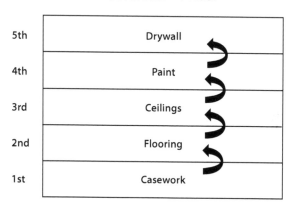

Trade	Drywall	Paint	Ceilings	Flooring	Casework
	Days to Completion				
1st Floor	5	10	15	20	25
2nd Floor	10	15	20	25	30
3rd Floor	15	20	25	30	35
4th Floor	20	25	30	35	40
5th Floor	25	30	35	40	45

The second diagram shows the impact of dividing the same scope of work into smaller batches. Our example uses a batch size of one-fifth of a floor. With that approach, the trades follow much closer together, and the casework installer starts their first batch on the fifth floor while the drywaller completes the last batch on the fifth floor. Each trade still takes five days per floor, but each is now just one day ahead of the next. This approach requires additional coordination and careful planning, but the results are almost always worth it. The project using the small-batch approach finishes in only twenty-nine days, a schedule reduction of 35%. Smaller batches ALWAYS move faster!

Batch Size = 1/5 of a Floor

5th	Casework	Flooring	Ceilings	Paint	Drywall
4th					
3rd					
2nd					
1st					

Trade	Drywall	Paint	Ceilings	Flooring	Casework
	Days to Completion				
1st Floor	5	6	7	8	9
2nd Floor	10	11	12	13	14
3rd Floor	15	16	17	18	19
4th Floor	20	21	22	23	24
5th Floor	25	26	27	28	29

In addition to moving faster, and this is critically important to dealing with variability, working in small batches allows the team to be much more responsive to changes and work interruptions. A colleague once toured a four-story senior living project as it neared completion. The project had been constructed in large batches, and there were obvious signs that this did not allow the team to respond well to unexpected conditions.

The project used a batch size of one full building floor, which included 32 one- and two-bedroom apartment units. After the framing crew completed one floor, it was turned over to the crews completing the sanitary drains and fire piping. When they completed their work on the floor, the HVAC contractor would take over. Next, the electrician was in to do their rough-in, along with the plumber to complete the hot and cold supply lines before turning each floor over to the drywaller. But when the plumber installed the first shower valve in the first unit on the first floor, they discovered a serious problem.

The stud framing had been laid out such that a double structural stud was located in the exact center of the showerhead wall—a simple oversight that had not been realized during the review of erection drawings. Changing the stud layout before framing started would have been simple to fix with no additional labor costs and no impact on the project schedule. But by the time the issue was discovered, the framing was nearly completed on the fourth and final floor of the building. After a careful survey of all apartment units, the general contractor determined that if the valves and showerheads were to be centered in the walls as planned, the studs would have to be relocated in over 120 shower walls throughout the building. The correction would cost about $40,000 and a two-week delay to the drywall work.

Their ultimate solution was to leave the studs as they were and offset the plumbing as needed. The result was a completed building where most of the shower valves and heads were oddly out of place. While it was not a problem for function of the showers, it gave an impression of shoddy craftsmanship that the rental agents had to explain to almost every potential tenant who toured the building.

If the same project had adopted a small-batch approach, where each trade was just a few days behind the next, this stud layout problem would have been discovered when there were only a few units framed out. The framer could have changed the design for future framing and circled back to correct the few units that had already been framed. The problem could have been resolved with minimal cost and almost no delay to construction. The large-batch approach limited the team's flexibility and stole their opportunity to deal with a simple quality issue without adding cost and time to the project.

Use Visible Buffers That the Team Shares

Installing buffers, such as extra inventory in a manufacturing plant or extra time in a project schedule, is a valid way to deal with unevenness or uncertainty in any workflow. A Toyota assembly plant today maintains enough parts inventory buffers to operate the plant for a couple of hours. While this is a drastic reduction from traditional plants that may have days or weeks worth of inventory, inventory buffers exist in even the leanest operation. The buffers are necessary to allow for small variations in the work and maintain smooth flow despite any unevenness in the assembly process.

In project work, there are two problems that make the use of buffers tricky. First, the buffers are often hard to see. While you can certainly see a bundle of pipe that sits on a project site for weeks before being installed, you cannot "see" the float that's inserted as a buffer in the schedule, or the contingency that is included in the duration of any individual task in a work plan. These are buffers of time used to protect against the uncertainty of project work.

The second problem with buffers in project work is that each team member often feels the need to have their own buffers to protect themselves and their company against the project's uncertainties. This results in the roofer asking for three weeks to do a two-week activity, the architect asking for twenty days to review a submittal, and a project owner demanding three months to make finish selections for the interiors of a building. In an industry where uncertainty and variation are rampant, this is understandable. However, rather than reducing variability, these types of buffers actually cover it up and add to the uncertainty of the project work. Combined, the cumulative effect of these types of buffers is that project leaders end up receiving materials weeks earlier than needed, demanding schedule cuts from every trade, and pushing the owner for decisions much earlier than is actually required to keep the work moving. Like a flick of the wrist creates a growing wave in a bullwhip, these hidden buffers build more unpredictability in the work until it is difficult to achieve any kind of reliable workflow.

To correct for these two challenges, limit the use of buffers in a controlled way that is visible to the team, and shared by all. Making time buffers visible is not difficult. On a construction schedule for a project to be built during a Minnesota winter, we always add an activity titled "lost work days for weather." If the team has even a bit of experience working in this region, they'll know on average how many days will be lost in the months of December, January, and February. Likewise, if the city approval process is notoriously difficult, it's smart to include a buffer in the design schedule for resubmittals and resolution of conflicts. The number will never be perfect, but it will relieve some of the fear individual trades may have so they feel more comfortable providing "real" task durations during project planning. We've found that when these kinds of shared time buffers are established early by the team, individual project performers are more likely to commit to shorter task durations during collaborative planning. The result is a project work plan that is shorter and more tightly coordinated between trades than one where hidden time contingencies are built into each task.

During execution of the work, the time buffer is used up when bad weather or other work disruptions are encountered. Usually, the shared buffer is more than adequate to accommodate the actual delays on the project. In addition, because the team has learned to plan and execute work in a collaborative way, they are much better at overcoming disruptions that do occur. We often see a spirit of teamwork emerge that enables teams to work around project delays without even needing to use the buffer. Armed with tools to manage the variability of the project together, the team becomes capable of a higher level of collaboration that allows each team member to achieve their own objectives within the team rather than in spite of it.

Make Decisions and Plans at the Last Responsible Moment

Those responsible for planning and managing projects have developed many approaches over recent decades to provide a sense of control. With the advent of computers, the Critical Path Method (CPM) of scheduling became (and remains) the most popular tool for planning work, especially on complex projects with long time frames. This approach attempts to plan, often in excruciating detail, the string of events that will lead to completing a project within the given time frame. It makes visible the path (or paths) of activities that drives the overall schedule and is key to meeting the targeted dates, the critical path of the project. Unfortunately, the only thing we know for certain about the work plan, as presented in a CPM schedule, is that it will turn out to be wrong! In fact, the more detail provided, and the further into the future the activities are planned, the more wrong the plan will be.

When a pharmaceutical manufacturer that relied on hyper-detailed CPM scheduling to plan the construction of a new manufacturing plant engaged our help they were four months into a 24-month project, and already two weeks behind schedule. We explained to project leaders our perspective that the CPM schedule was largely full of assumptions and guesses. We pointed to activities set for sixteen months into the future that provided details about installing a specific control valve or completing a pressure test for a single process piping line. We asked, "If the work happening today is off by two weeks, what confidence do you have that these future activities will occur in any way that resembles the CPM schedule?"

The project scheduler and project manager were adamant about the need for such detailed scheduling and began to scour the 10,000 tasks of the CPM schedule for examples of critical work activities that absolutely had to be scheduled in fine detail far in advance. They were convinced that tasks incorporating materials with long lead times would prove their point about the need for this type of detailed, advance scheduling. My colleague noticed a line in the schedule that called for a pump with a three-month delivery lead time to be installed the next week. When he asked how well this CPM schedule helped them prepare for and procure that pump on time, the scheduler and PM looked at each other sheepishly.

First, the scheduler acknowledged that the pump could not actually be set for another four months because they had discovered a sequencing conflict as the mechanics prepared the anchoring frame earlier in the week. Next, the project manager admitted that the pump was actually delivered on site eight weeks prior because procurement had been afraid the schedule was underestimating the speed at which the work would progress. Both the scheduler and PM acknowledged that their approach to scheduling left a lot of room for improvement.

When applying lean thinking to projects, we teach teams to delay planning to the last responsible moment, the point in time where delaying further could jeopardize progress. This means that we do not develop a detailed schedule far in advance. Instead, we use a high-level milestone schedule as a guide. This milestone schedule identifies the major phases of the project, addresses long lead items, and establishes the promise of the project, confirming that the owner's overall objectives can actually be met.

More detailed planning happens as the start of each phase approaches. By that time, the people who will do the work are engaged and paying attention, and much of the unknowns from earlier phases have been resolved. The team creates this phase plan with the requirement that it meets the phase completion due date set forth in the milestone schedule. They plan collaboratively as they think through starting the work. The result is a more detailed plan that can actually be implemented as planned.

Finally, just before each week's work is executed, the team creates an even more detailed plan, which defines the work for each day of the following week. This weekly work plan is more detailed than even a traditional CPM schedule, but it is only made a few days in advance. The team has strong confidence that the work can be completed as planned, and it allows them to execute the work smoothly each day in alignment with the project's broad objectives. This just-in-time approach to scheduling provides the team maximum flexibility to deal with design changes and other surprises along the way, variability that could never be anticipated or accounted for in a CPM schedule created months in advance.

We use a similar approach for decision-making in project work. By delaying decisions to the last responsible moment, the team does not waste time analyzing and deciding on issues based on partial information or ungrounded assumptions. When decisions are made too early, we find that the team has no confidence in them, and ends up changing, or at least reconsidering, many of them. I saw a simple building project re-evaluate its decision about mechanical systems every month for the entire six-month duration of the design process, as information about the structure and building envelope evolved. Each time, the time, energy, and money that they spent was wasted on a plan that was eventually discarded. By delaying such decisions, project teams can greatly soften the impact of the uncertainty inherent in the design process and gain the flexibility to respond to real information as it becomes available.

Many project-driven teams have used these strategies to conquer variability and create a smooth workflow that once seemed unattainable.

I've heard project managers, superintendents, foremen, and executives say the same thing: "I'll never go back to my firefighting ways—this is a better way to deliver projects and a better way to work."

Open your thinking to two new ideas. First, variation in project work is not inevitable. You can have more impact to reduce it than you might imagine. Second, you can manage the variation and uncertainty that remain in a way that maintains flexibility while supporting smooth workflow. The two ideas, when employed together, make a powerful combination that can help every project-driven organization conquer variability.

———

3

Fast-Launching Teams

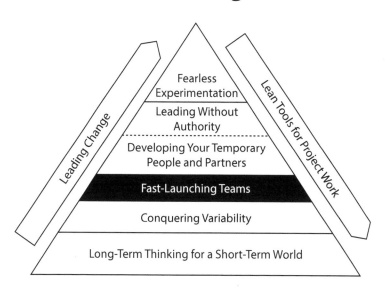

EVERY PROJECT REQUIRES A team, and every team, at any particular time, is performing at some level of proficiency against the objectives of the project. In steady-state lean operations, the team is always improving and building on their previous learning. Over time, a team reaches a level of performance that enables it to meet or exceed the needs of the organization.

Project work does not have this luxury of time. Project teams form quickly, execute the work for some limited duration of time, and then disband when the project is complete, going on to form new teams on the next project. For projects to be successful, it's essential that teams reach a high level of performance very quickly. Any time spent ramping up or learning how to function as a team detracts from the project's success.

Rocket vs. Airplane

I was eating lunch with group of leaders for a large, complex design and construction project. We were congratulating ourselves on our progress—helping a team adopt lean practices in an attempt to lower costs, shorten durations, and reduce disruptive quality issues that had been hampering the project. In just three months, the team had adopted new norms of behavior that were beginning to pay big dividends. The team had coalesced around a set of project "Conditions of Satisfaction,"[11] which they were using to guide strategy and make quick, effective decisions. The team had a process for bringing problems to the surface quickly and was beginning to deal with issues transparently and openly. They were starting to behave like a high-performing lean team. Productivity was up, and things were getting done in less time. A new lean culture was taking root.

One of our coaching partners joined the group and listened quietly to our enthusiasm for what was happening. We compared the project team to an airplane gaining speed down the runway. We were excited to see the momentum building and anticipated the imminent liftoff.

"You do realize that we're three months into this six-month project phase, don't you?" He interjected, "There's no more time here for building speed on the runway. We need a rocket, not an airplane!"

He was right. While the team's progress was impressive, much of the improvement would not benefit the phase of project we were in. The improved team performance already came too late to help the

---

[11] Fernando Flores, *Conversations For Action and Collected Essays: Instilling a Culture of Commitment in Working Relationships* (self-pub., CreateSpace Independent Publishing Platform, 2012). The term "Conditions of Satisfaction" refers to a central component of the Conversations for Action model developed by Fernando Flores, presented in a series of essays between 1985 and 2000. The idea of establishing project Conditions of Satisfaction, and other of Flores' concepts, have been adopted by building teams using the Integrated Project Delivery approach.

first half of the phase, and the team would probably not hit full stride until near the end.

The rocket vs. airplane analogy has stuck with me ever since.

In his model for team development, educational psychologist Bruce Tuckman argues that teams must pass through stages as they learn to function together.[12] Team performance evolves from forming to storming to norming before finally reaching the performing stage. Because project teams are temporary, and have to become high-performing in a tight time frame, we need ways to shorten the time to high-performance. Further, ineffective teamwork and poor coordination are two of the biggest barriers to successful projects, leading to schedule delays, low productivity, high costs, dangerous working conditions, and often a very unsatisfying work experience for participants at all levels. In project work, the ability to build high-functioning teams quickly is not just a nice idea. For project-driven organizations, it's an essential strategic capability.

The goal in project work is to develop high-performing teams you'd find in a successful lean operation such as Toyota. Here, teams understand the standard work, strive to improve processes, are empowered and expected to rapidly uncover and solve problems, and operate in an environment of trust and respect. As a result, they have minimal quality issues, better safety performance, and incredible levels of productivity. Lean operations have a huge strategic advantage over their non-lean competitors. In the project-driven environment we're pursuing the same kind of high-performing team, we just need to find a way to get there faster. We need a vertical takeoff.

The concepts presented here can rapidly elicit the desired team behavior by properly setting the stage and creating an environment where teamwork and lean thinking are the norm, not the exception.

---

[12] Angelo Kinicki and Robert Kreitner, *Organizational Behavior: Key Concepts, Skills & Best Practices* (New York: McGraw-Hill Companies, Inc., 2003), 204.

We have not given up on transformative improvement. Rather, we've learned ways to help project teams "get to good" much faster. These strategies help teams launch like a rocket.

Visual Management Sets the Stage

Visual management (or visual control) is a staple of lean management. Walk into a lean manufacturing plant, and you're bound to see the walls covered with standard work descriptions, status reports for improvement initiatives, and brightly colored charts comparing actual work progress to planned. Making standards and metrics visual, and teaching all to manage their work and communicate openly *through* the information helps everyone, from managers to front-line workers, understand the work standard and know immediately if they are deviating from it. This approach provides quick feedback about work status, uncovers systematic problems, and encourages continuous improvement of work processes. It also creates a culture of openness and transparency where information is shared automatically, and individuals come to expect that their successes and failures will be used to help others learn.

In project-driven organizations, however, leaders sometimes get it wrong. Too often, they try to use visual management as a reporting tool that forces accountability and pressures individuals to conform. When the pressure is on to improve performance, leaders sometimes tighten the screws by adding more metrics, hiring data collectors, and singling out poor performers.

For example, a typical visual reporting opportunity on construction projects is to post the Percent Plan Complete (PPC),[13] a metric that reflects a team's ability to reliably plan and execute weekly work. I

---

[13] PPC is one part of the Last Planner® System described more fully in the Chapter 8. Last Planner is a registered trademark of Lean Construction Institute.

once saw a project leadership team use this potentially positive tool to destroy teamwork and create animosity among subcontractors. Instead of having the team members self-report on their progress and identify areas for improvement, the leaders created a team of "observers" to evaluate each trade contractor's performance without their input. As a result of the collected data, the leaders singled out poor performers without understanding the root causes of the problems and demanded improvement from individuals under threat of contractual penalties. In an environment where a feeling of unity and teamwork was already elusive, this drove a wedge between individuals, and rewarded those who optimized their own silos, while providing zero incentive to first work in the best interest of the collective project. Visual management applied in this way does not support teamwork and is not lean.

To understand how visual management can be applied to build effective project-driven teams, first think about how it's applied in a traditional lean environment. In a traditional (steady-state) lean environment, teamwork is baked into the culture over years, and visual controls focus on the processes for performing value-added work—"pick up one bolt from the bin with your left hand, insert it into the jig, apply the driver with your right hand, tighten until the clutch clicks, return the driver to the holster." The process is wildly effective for maintaining consistent quality and improving processes, but is not typically employed specifically to strengthen teamwork. However, we've found that in the project environment, we can also apply visual management with a slightly different focus as a tool to quickly build effective teams.

To leverage visual management for creating fast-launching teams, you can make one simple adjustment. Instead of focusing the visual controls on only standardizing and improving the value-added work, use it to also standardize and improve the *team performance*. At the same time, challenge the team to create and manage the visual controls themselves to help them build capacity for self-management and improve their team performance.

For example, if you want your teams to have effective, collaborative meetings, create visual controls that support the right behavior. Challenge the team to create a standard meeting agenda with time limits for each topic. Post the agenda on the wall next to a clock, and encourage the meeting leader to recruit another team member to act as timekeeper. If meeting attendance is an issue, the team can create an attendance check-in sheet. As each member arrives, they self-report whether their arrival is on time or late. The meeting leader asks the group to confirm which members are missing as they check "absent" for the unreported participants. The team will quickly learn that meetings follow a standard process, and that team members have the opportunity and obligation to improve the meeting process.

Another common problem in project work is that individuals have generally learned to avoid making commitments to each other. This may seem like an overstatement, but pay attention to the next conversation you hear on a project. It may sound something like this:

Paul: John, I need an answer to that design question, so I can finish this part of the program.
John: Yes, I know. I should be able to work on it later this week.
Paul: This is really critical, I'm practically shut down until I get an answer.
John: I know, it's at the top of my list.
Paul: Do you know when I can expect your answer?
John: I'm working on it. Hopefully this week.
Paul: OK, let me know when it's ready.

At first glance, this may seem like the two men came to some sort of workable agreement, but, upon closer examination, we see that no one made any commitments in this exchange. And the outcome is clear as mud. When does Paul need his answer? When will John provide it? Who knows. These two "teammates" have talked right past each other, and no one really has a clue how or when the issue will be resolved. On most projects, this type of conversation happens dozens of times each day and gets carried forward week after week, leading to prolonged delays and rising costs.

We use visual management to correct this behavior, and get teams asking for and making commitments. By posting a commitment log in the team's meeting space, all team members understand and follow the process for resolving problems by requesting and making commitments. The log has a place to describe the issue (Paul needs an answer to a design question), a place for Paul to identify his need date, a place to record who is taking responsibility for resolution, and a date when it will be resolved. Using this visual tool, the conversation changes to this:

Paul: John, I need an answer to that design question, so I can finish this part of the program.
John: Yikes, I'm swamped. When do you need it?
Paul: It's holding up my work now. Can you finish it Wednesday?
John: I can't promise Wednesday, but I know I can get it to you by Friday.
Paul: OK. I'll switch to another task until Friday. Can you commit to Friday?
John: Yes, put me down for Friday on the commitment log.

This exchange takes no more time than the previous example, but in this version, both parties know what to expect so they can plan their work around real information and have confidence that they can trust their teammate to deliver.

Designing a standard process for resolving issues, and making the process visual, helps team members adopt the desired behavior without a lot of training or lecturing. Clients often tell us that adopting this type of visual resolution process is a turning point in their team's effectiveness.

Visual management is not just about the information that's posted on the wall. It is a system for gathering, updating, and reporting information that empowers individuals and supports a lean culture. As a launching tool for teams, visual controls can set the stage and provide important cues to acceptable behavior. If a team establishes these processes early, each new member immediately understands how they'll have to behave to fit in.

When we go in to work with an organization, we get management to think about behaviors that are lacking and lead their teams to devise the visual management processes to standardize and improve them. When a team creates these processes themselves, they become committed to the standard and readily share it with others. You'd be surprised how fast this process can raise a team's effectiveness.

Leaders Must Model the Right Behavior (and Recruit Followers)

Visual controls by themselves can help create powerful cues for team behavior, but without strong leadership, teams will learn to ignore them. It's critical that team leaders model the desired behavior and expect the same from others. In this way, one individual can have a powerful influence over a team's performance.

I was asked to help a group of middle managers responsible for delivering a series of construction projects in rapid succession. They had become frustrated by their team members' lack of focus, as they missed one completion milestone after another. The team was capable of getting the work done, but they seemed to ignore project schedule priorities. Like individuals on many failing projects, they had become numb to the daily "fire drills" and constant change of priorities that the project had devolved into. They learned to expect that work could not be planned and executed with any reliability. The project was beginning to spiral into chaos.

As one part of the solution, we coached managers to model the right behaviors when interacting with team members. This meant they needed to show up on time for meetings, stay focused on important conversations, ask about and understand milestones, and pay attention when team members raised concerns. By modeling these productive behaviors, each manager was switching the mindset of his team from one of hopelessness to control. Team members were beginning to understand that they could influence the project, and that they didn't have to fight fires all day every day.

I was preparing one of these managers for a meeting with his boss, Andre, a hard-driving command-and-control style leader who had a notoriously short attention span and a reputation for texting and emailing during meetings. It took us two weeks to secure a 30-minute meeting on Andre's calendar, and we knew it would be our only chance to focus his attention on broad issues that were impacting the team's ability to complete their work.

As the meeting started, Andre was immediately distracted by an incoming text. We tried to keep the conversation going, but the text was followed by an email, and he was thumbing a reply on his phone. I knew we had to find a way to turn the meeting around. I'd been working with the manager on modeling acceptable behavior, and we quickly found ourselves putting this new skill into practice with his boss.

Each time Andre began reading or typing on his phone, we simply stopped talking. He didn't much notice at first, but after a few pauses in the conversation he urged us, "keep talking, I'm listening."

Our response: "That's OK, we'll wait."

It took just three or four awkward pauses in the conversation before Andre realized that he could not continue his disruptive behavior in this environment. After less than five minutes, he put his phone in his pocket and gave us his full attention for the rest of the meeting. Afterward, the manager told me he'd never seen his boss put away his phone—ever. We'd accomplished a dramatic improvement in behavior in a surprisingly short time.

This is an example of how we can improve behavior and team results quickly by modeling what is acceptable. We did not lecture the boss on why his behavior was unacceptable. We did not create a poster that said, "no phones during meetings." We didn't even ask the boss to put away his phone. In reality, those efforts had been tried many times with this individual with no effect. Instead, we created an environment where the correct and expected behavior was obvious. In this environment, behaving outside the norms became very uncomfortable, even for the boss.

We've used a similar approach to improve team behavior in other situations. When one member, Steve, was consistently letting his teammates down by not providing his work plan in time for weekly meetings, the leaders learned to stop the meeting and ask him to create it live, during the meeting. The rest of the team was frustrated by the delay, but they needed accurate information in their work plan, so they were willing to wait. At the same time, Steve realized he was holding up the entire planning process and irritating his teammates. After doing this "live update" in one or two meetings, he started coming prepared.

By modeling the right team behavior in an obvious and open way, and even exaggerating the desired behavior, leaders can build that behavior into the culture of the team. It's an important leadership skill, and a proven way to improve team performance—fast.

Followers Are Key to Success
(Why Dread Pirate Roberts Will Live Forever)

In the book (and later the film) *The Princess Bride*, Dread Pirate Roberts, as the name suggests, was a notorious pirate who was as loved by his crew as he was feared by other seamen. He had a reputation so fierce that ships surrendered their bounty without a fight—a pretty good life for a pirate! The story of how Roberts achieved such success, and was able to maintain his position for decades, provides valuable lessons for those who set out to build fast-launching teams.

When Wesley, our story's young hero, explained to Buttercup, his longtime love, that he was actually the Dread Pirate Roberts, something didn't add up. Buttercup knew that Roberts had been terrorizing the sea for decades, but Wesley had only been away for a few years. There is no way Wesley could be the notorious pirate. Or was there?

Wesley went on to reveal his secret. Wesley's ship had actually been captured by Roberts five years prior. Roberts had taken Wesley as his only prisoner and put him to work as cabin boy. Over time, Wesley and Roberts developed a close friendship. Roberts taught Wesley all he knew about the pirate life—how to run a ship, how to maintain a fearsome reputation, and how to manage a crew of dangerous misfits.

When Wesley was ready, Roberts made him an offer. At its next stop in port, the pirate ship would release the entire crew. Only Roberts and Wesley would remain. Together, they would recruit an entirely new crew before embarking on their next journey. However, to the new crew, Wesley would be known as Dread Pirate Roberts and Roberts would serve as his cabin boy. As the "follower" Roberts would reinforce Wesley's authority as captain and make it clear to the crew that he was not to be questioned or challenged. Thus, overnight,

Wesley gained the respect and power that Roberts had taken a lifetime to develop.

When they reached the next port a few weeks later, Roberts left the ship and went on to a comfortable retirement. Wesley adopted a new cabin boy and continued as Dread Pirate Roberts with no one ever suspecting the substitution had taken place. Wesley had no idea how many times this transition had occurred, but he knew that when he was ready to return home to Buttercup, he had a way to ensure that Dread Pirate Roberts would live on.

While the story of Dread Pirate Roberts is amusing, it illustrates an important point. Followers are essential and must be part of any plan to create effective teams. Additionally, if you don't have the luxury of building team performance over a long period of time, the role of followers should be deliberately planned and executed to support your leadership and model proper behavior for others. In our consulting business, we are often faced with the challenge of helping a team leader gain the trust and confidence of their project team, as they try to instill effective behaviors in a short amount of time. One of the techniques we use is that of the effective follower. By helping the leader's boss or other key team members understand the importance of following, we quickly boost their effectiveness and the effectiveness of the team. The leader models the behavior, for example, that we expect reliable commitments from each other and statements like "I hope to" or "I should be able to" are not acceptable.

When the leader hears this type of fuzzy language, they declare, "That doesn't work here. I need a reliable commitment." If this is all that happens, it's easy for team members to roll their eyes and underestimate the power of this shift in team language. However, when a respected follower joins the effort, the team starts to see this is not just the desire of a single person; it's a norm that must be followed.

When the follower asks for clarification on the concept, the leader has a chance to explain it for everyone. When the team sees the follower asking for and accepting advice from the leader, their influence with the team immediately doubles. When the follower starts to emulate the behavior of the leader, the movement gains momentum again. When one or two additional team members get on board with the new behaviors, the team has reached a tipping point. Very quickly, the team has adopted a new way of thinking and talking about getting things done. A new norm has been established, and team members expect it from each other and teach it to new members. This new norm can be maintained with little effort, and new team members readily understand how this team has decided to behave. The group has become a self-managing team that expects certain things from its members.

Identifying followers and helping them understand the importance of their roles is the first step. Don't leave it to chance or just assume that your key people will fill this role successfully by default. Make sure the leader and follower agree on the objectives and are deliberate about how they'll get there. Try becoming a follower for one of your subordinates. The approach works whether you're helping a CFO get what he needs from the board, or helping a new foreman gain the confidence of his crew.

Onboarding on Purpose

When new members join a team, which happens constantly in project work, they are always "indoctrinated" into the group norms. They learn where the lunchroom is, how to submit their time sheet, and what behavior is expected. While much of this indoctrination can happen on the fly, especially when the team norms are visual and well established, it's critical not to leave important elements to chance.

On most construction projects, for example, new employees are required to go through site safety orientation before being allowed to work on site. They usually watch a video or presentation about evacuation procedures, location of MSDS sheets, and specific hazards that exist on the job. They might learn specific rules for working in the location, like not parking in the employee lot, or making sure to eat only in the designated break areas. All projects conduct this training because everyone on the job must possess a basic level of understanding. It cannot be left to chance, and individuals can't be allowed to flounder or risk injury while they figure it out.

Additionally, on lean projects, team members must also understand new ways of behaving and new concepts for planning and executing work. Unfortunately, many powerful lean concepts are completely foreign to most members of project teams. They are accustomed to traditional management approaches and have learned over time that it's best to keep problems to themselves, follow orders, and protect their own company's bottom line over the interests of the project. Changing the expectations for these team members will take more than a 20-minute video. An effective onboarding process can ensure that individuals understand what's expected and reinforce the norms that have been purposefully established on the project.

When we plan the onboarding process for a lean project's team members, we rely on three main concepts. First, the onboarding must be an experience, not a lecture. You can talk to people forever about the benefits of lean, but until they actually feel the difference, they just won't get it. Second, most of the learning happens in practice, in the real work environment. This builds a practical understanding of concepts and makes lean practices habitual. Finally, onboarding is not an individual experience. Team members must be connected to others, so they can learn that they're expected to ask for help and improve over time. Working in pairs or within a small cohort group, individuals learn effective team behavior.

Each project has unique constraints that can challenge an onboarding program. Every project struggles with the time commitment, no matter how small, of taking team members away from their work to learn something new. In reality, the time spent onboarding pays off many times over as the individuals, and the collective team, benefit from improved performance, and find themselves on a much faster path to effectiveness. A good onboarding program includes the following elements.

Experiential Learning

We design onboarding sessions to include small numbers of project participants in mixed groups. We want workers learning alongside managers, and subcontractors interacting with designers and representatives of the project owner. This experience, which we usually call a boot camp, is the first opportunity to demonstrate that the project is a team effort.

The boot camp can range in duration from a couple of lunch 'n' learn sessions to a full three-day immersive experience. Whatever the time frame, the key is for the participants to *experience* the behavior that is expected of them. With simple group exercises, individuals can experience the impact of lean concepts such as small-batch thinking, a focus on flow instead of productivity, or the power of reliable commitments. We employ numerous lean simulations and exercises appropriate for this purpose. The exercises allow design and construction teams to experience first-hand the positive effects of working in small batches, reducing variation, or even running a project on the Last Planner® System.

Whatever the exercise, it's critical to connect the concepts to the work at hand. For our clients' teams, we use simulations to start a conversation about what is possible on *this* project. What could small batches look like? How could we apply a pull system? How could reducing the work-in-process inventory speed up the work and improve quality at the same time? We select the exercises that work for the specific project, within the time constraints. We engage the participants in this experience and let them see for themselves what happens when lean concepts are applied to their work. Since all team members go through the same exercise, they share a common experience to draw upon as they learn to work together.

By building onboarding sessions around a simulation or game, we create a memorable experience for each individual that begins to shift their mindset from traditional to lean thinking. We often use a production system design simulation we call "The Airplane Game." It's a team exercise that demonstrates how lean concepts can improve any production process. After building Lego® airplanes in a traditional batch and queue system, participants get to apply several lean improvements to the assembly process. They might not remember the theory behind single piece flow, or why a lean operation has so little inventory in the system, but they will forever remember that smaller batches always move faster, and that the lean operation out-performs the traditional approach with higher quality, lower cost, faster delivery, and a much safer work environment. We've created an understanding that will stick with them. When the team later needs to make improvements, they will instinctively, and very quickly, draw upon that understanding without needing to look it up in a training manual. We're building a common understanding and competence within the team through the onboarding experience.

Learning through Practice

Learning new behaviors can be converted into habit if the behavior is applied quickly and consistently in practice. If done well, the experience that team members have in an onboarding session will stick with them throughout the project. For teams to apply new concepts to their daily work, they need support to overcome the "gravity" of old practices and accelerate that team's momentum. We use coaches to provide this support. A coach, whether outside the company or an internal resource, is not the team leader. Instead a coach is someone who is responsible to demonstrate, model, and reinforce the correct use of the process in action for the team. They become a trusted resource and act as a sounding board for practical issues that come up while a team is adopting new behaviors. Although serving as a coach requires some specific skills, it is not necessarily a full-time job.

At one company that was applying new lean behaviors across a series of twenty projects simultaneously, we recruited and trained a team of internal coaches to provide this support. Each coach had worked in the new process themselves on previous projects and understood the challenges of making a broad change in team behavior. They also had experienced the benefits of the new approach firsthand and had confidence that it could improve the company's overall performance.

Each project team was assigned a coach, who would attend key events such as weekly meetings, planning sessions, or performance reviews. The coach collaborated with the project leader to build their competence and confidence with the new processes. The coach used their own experience to help the leader work through specific issues and drew upon deeper knowledge (from within the organization or from our firm if needed) if he encountered an unfamiliar challenge.

The coach became the leader's connection to a safety net that allowed him to move fearlessly into an unknown future.

Before deploying coaches to support new behaviors, consider some vital ground rules. First, the coaches have no authority on the project, and should never interfere with or challenge the position of project leaders. Coaches are there to support the lean process and new behaviors, not to help run the project. I'll discuss this idea of leading without authority in a later chapter.

Second, prior to coaching any individual, a coach must acquire their permission. This can be accomplished in a quick initial conversation that sets the parameters of the coaching work. It's most effective for the coach to provide live feedback and guidance to the team while they are completing their work. However, if the coach does not secure permission to do this in advance, their input can be disruptive and undermine the authority of team leaders.

Finally, as a support mechanism for the team and its leader, a coach can have a powerful influence even with limited contact. In some cases, we've utilized coaches who are leading their own projects to support a new team by interacting for only one or two hours per week. After just a few weeks, the team adopts the new behaviors and functions in the new process at a very high level.

The coaching process is very effective in helping teams adopt new lean practices and build confidence and competence. This relatively small effort dramatically increases the likelihood of change in team behavior and the desired improvement in performance that comes with it. After this initial support, the team is ready to supplement the coaching with a different type of support—improving and maintaining together.

Improving and Maintaining Together

As a team improves, it's important for the team leader to have a network of other lean thinkers to provide encouragement and prevent back-sliding into old habits. This type of network, usually developed within one company or project organization, provides a place for leaders to discuss their challenges and victories, air their frustrations, and learn from others' experience.

This network does not have to be elaborate to prevent the feeling of isolation that leaders often encounter. In fact, it can be as simple as two team leaders who visit each other's project every few weeks in a structured way.

As an organization applies new lean processes on several projects, the leaders can develop a short list of what the new process should look like—a standard for the behaviors, visuals, and outcomes that they expect. This list can be used as a simple assessment tool for the leaders to understand their team's progress and help them think about which adjustments might be needed. When leaders share their assessment tools with one another and ask for feedback, they can create an organic collaboration network that provides support and spurs improvements across multiple projects at the same time.

At one company, we asked each project leader to visit one other project every month and complete an assessment. During the visits, the leaders discussed challenges, reviewed progress, and shared honest feedback. They learned to discuss the processes being used to get results rather than the day-to-day events of the projects.

This type of networking can have a dramatic effect on the culture of a company. Project leaders become more open and less guarded about what is happening in their own world. They learn to get and give honest feedback by focusing on processes rather than people. By working this way with their peers, they become more effective at bringing issues higher into the organization when there is a problem, quickly summoning help from the organizational layer that can most effectively deal with each issue. They collectively become a force for change in culture not only within their projects, but for the organization as a whole.

Conclusion

A colleague once made the comment that "lean concepts are very simple, but people are complicated." Rapidly building high-performing teams is no different. While the concepts presented here are simple on the surface, they take practice to perfect. The good news is that you don't need to have it all figured out to start making real progress.

As you work to shorten your teams' time to liftoff, focus on the basics. Teach your people how to lead and how to follow. Employ visual management processes to display, and even exaggerate, the norms that have been adopted by the team, and use onboarding as an opportunity to get new team members off on the right foot. Each element increases the speed at which individuals begin performing like a team. Incorporate all of them effectively, and you'll build teams that take off like a rocket.

———

4

Developing Your Temporary People and Partners

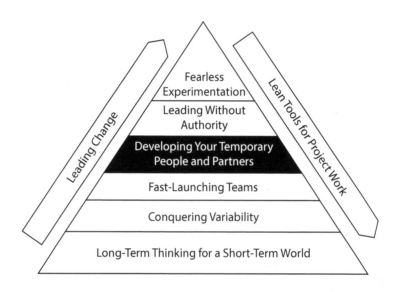

IN LEAN ORGANIZATIONS, DEVELOPING people and partners is a central focus of management and leadership at every level. These organizations understand that they cannot grow or improve without growing and developing those who do the work of the organization. In most cases, this work is not accomplished by only the company's employees; it is accomplished by a complex web of employees working with consultants, contractors, suppliers, and others, without whom the mission of the organization could not be achieved. For this reason, developing only the employees of the organization is far from adequate to get the continuous improvement needed to succeed and thrive. In fact, learning to develop both the people within your organization and the partners outside your company is an essential capability for any lean enterprise.

Developing employees is something most companies are paying attention to. However, some make the mistake of thinking of this as the work of HR or a training department. In those companies, people development is usually limited to training sessions, educational programs, and certifications in specific skills important to the company. While these elements are useful for relaying knowledge, what's missing is the critical component of personal growth and development. People best learn to put knowledge into action when they apply it to their actual work.

Think of a time you tried to teach someone, a child or a friend, a skill that you had already mastered. Would you teach someone to ride a bike by explaining the physics of balance and motion? Of course not. You might explain a few basics, like "make sure to always wear your helmet," and "pedal backward to brake," but the real learning happens only while actually sitting on a bike. That's where the understanding and skill are developed, and eventually mastered. In the same way, we should not expect employees to gain and master new skills except by practice on their actual work.

The most effective employee development programs rely on coaching, mentoring, and supporting people as they apply learning in practice, and creating an environment where learning and growth are not only encouraged but expected of everyone at every level. This takes the responsibility for people development away from the HR department and puts it squarely on the shoulders of every manager in the organization. Foremen are responsible for the growth of those working in their crews, supervisors are responsible for the growth of the foremen, and managers are responsible for developing those working in their departments. In this environment, learning and personal development are incorporated into the work itself, and not treated as a separate function. The issue of developing employees in a lean organization is addressed quite nicely in several books and is not my focus in this chapter.[14]

My purpose here is to address the gap that most project-driven organizations are either blind to or just have no way to deal with: how to develop the companies and people outside your organization who are essential to completing your work. These "temporary people," although they are only engaged with your company intermittently, should be considered partners who are at least as important to your success as your employees. Before we get into how, I will answer the question that usually gets asked first, "Why should I?"

Most project-driven companies don't try to develop people who are not "their own." They think of those who work for their suppliers, subcontractors, and consultants as disconnected from the company's long-term goals, and only engage them to achieve the short-term objectives of each project. These people, although they make up over 80% of workers on many projects, are often viewed as a fixed commodity that cannot be influenced or developed in any meaningful way over the course of a single project. This thinking leads project-driven organizations to miss out on the opportunity to challenge, mentor, and grow the people who play the biggest part in delivering the project—an oversight that limits the team's ability to perform at its highest level on any given project, and more broadly, its ability to improve from one project to the next. People, especially those closest to the work, are the most flexible, powerful source of continuous improvement in any work process. Neglecting any group of people is a fundamental

---

[14] Jeffrey K. Liker and Gary L. Convis, *The Toyota Way to Lean Leadership: Achieving and Sustaining Excellence Through Leadership Development* (New York: McGraw-Hill Education, 2011); Peter M. Senge, *The Fifth Discipline: the Art & Practice of the Learning Organization* (New York: Doubleday, 1990). Suggested reading about developing employees in a lean organization.

mistake, and a real tragedy when the contractors or consultants make up such a large part of the project team.

Early in my career, I worked on a construction project where the superintendent focused daily on the labor hours of his own employees: three foremen and a handful of men who were responsible for temporary controls on the project site. They would erect and move temporary partitions, manage traffic into and out of the site, operate the temporary elevator, and maintain the office trailers, break areas and other shared resources on the site. This superintendent made certain that his people were productive and he refused to add staff, even when they were falling behind in their work. His primary objective was to make sure he didn't overspend on this small piece that was under his direct control.

As the project progressed, it became clear that this small crew was inadequate to manage the amount of work required of them. The elevator, which really should have been running at least twelve hours per day to accommodate all the vertical transportation needs of the 300 people working on the project, was limited to eight hours per day to avoid overtime costs for the operator. Inadequate traffic control and poorly maintained roadways meant that deliveries took twice as long as needed, and this often slowed installation crews that were starved of the materials they needed. Because the superintendent put the interests of his people ahead of the needs of those working for subcontractors and suppliers, the overall project suffered. Schedules slipped, morale on the site declined, and overtime hours became standard for most crews. At the end of the project, the general contractor defended itself against claims from many subcontractors for added costs due to inadequate site management, and argued with the project owner about who was responsible for late completion and cost overruns. By focusing so intently on the small piece of the work performed by his employees, the superintendent cost the project tens of thousands of dollars, and created a miserable work environment for everyone.

In the same way, focusing development and growth efforts on just your own employees misses the forest for the trees. Growth and development must reach into your partners' organizations and impact how their people accomplish their work. Until learning is driven to every person who completes value-added work on every project, you are only tapping into part of the benefit of continuous improvement.

I've been using the term "partner" as a synonym for subcontractors, consultants, suppliers, and other non-employees who help deliver your project work. This term is often used loosely, and it's important to understand what it really means in a lean environment. Toyota provides a nice template for how we can think of these people and organizations as partners.

While not a purely project-driven organization, Toyota executes plenty of projects that support its manufacturing operations. Developing new technologies, introducing new models, and building new facilities are all examples of project work that Toyota relies upon for its ongoing success. Toyota continually works to develop the people employed by its contractors and suppliers, and has dedicated an entire division, the Toyota Supplier Support Center (TSSC), to help companies develop their people, improve operations, and become more valuable partners for Toyota. Treating these contractors as partners means that rather than continually shopping for new suppliers and lower prices, Toyota is committed to improving their suppliers, which includes developing their people. To make this possible, Toyota fosters long-term partnerships with a limited number of suppliers for each category of parts or services, and builds their partners' capacity in alignment with Toyota's own growth. Together, they can achieve growth and efficiencies that would be impossible by just shopping for cheaper suppliers.

These high-performance companies and the people who work in them are tightly integrated into Toyota's operations and improvement efforts. As a result, they understand Toyota and have the capability and flexibility to serve as true partners, even bailing them out in times of need.

On March 11, 2011, Japan was hit with an earthquake and tsunami that killed over 20,000 people and crippled the country's manufacturing economy.[15] Widespread power outages, structural damage, and destruction of transportation infrastructure led many industry analysts to predict that Toyota's operations would not return to full strength for a year or more, and that the disruption would have severe impacts on Toyota's automotive production around the globe. Since some of Toyota's critical parts suppliers were completely destroyed, it's easy to see why such predictions were made.

However, Toyota's network of suppliers is different from most of its competitors. Toyota treats suppliers as partners and considers the fate of partner companies as directly tied to its own. Rather than looking for replacement suppliers, Toyota doubled down on these partnerships and got even more value in return. Since most Japanese manufacturing and assembly plants were shut down due to damage, power outages, or lack of incoming supplies, many workers in Japanese companies were asked to stay home, basically being laid off without pay until the plants could be made operational again. This was not the case at Toyota.[16] Any assembly worker who wanted to work could volunteer to receive full salary by working to restore operations at any one of several of Toyota's partners' plants. Toyota workers, including

---

[15] George Olcott and Nick Oliver, "Japan's Tsunami Supply Chain Comeback," *Financial Times*, August 1, 2011, https://www.ft.com/content/c531d416-bc6b-11e0-acb6-00144feabdc0.

[16] Jason Lancaster, "How Toyota Recovered From the Earthquake Twice as Fast as Anyone Thought Possible," Tundra Headquarters (blog), June 24, 2011, http://www.tundraheadquarters.com/blog/toyota-recovery-earthquake-fast/.

assemblers, managers, and engineers went to work (at Toyota's expense) in their partners' plants to restore operations as quickly as possible.

At the same time, the partner suppliers reached out to their own networks, including their competitors, to find temporary replacement manufacturing capability for specific components of Toyota's vehicles. One part at a time, they found sources for everything from alternators to windshields that was needed to bring manufacturing back up to speed. They focused on one plant at time, first making sure that facilities outside of Japan were supplied with the parts needed to keep assembling vehicles. With operations at those plants secured, they worked to get plants in Japan up and running again quickly.

The natural disaster was devastating to Japan and to the auto industry as a whole. However, because Toyota was able to leverage its network of partners to help with the recovery, the damage was much less than outsiders had predicted. The impact to overseas plants was minimized, and most locations experienced minimal disruptions— all being resolved in a matter of days. By August or September, Toyota's Japanese manufacturing operations were back to pre-disaster levels. It was an impossible task made possible through the use of partners, developed and trained by Toyota over decades, to work seamlessly with the needs of the organization. The recovery took about half the time predicted and led to even stronger relationships and more resilient networks than existed before. Toyota's response to this disaster demonstrates how partners are much more than just companies to do business with. These long-term relationships are at the core of the organization's success, and their futures are inextricably linked.

Appealing as this all sounds, in the project-driven environment, I often hear leaders explain that they can't possibly use the same approach with their suppliers.

"We use different suppliers and subcontractors on every project."

"Our relationships are temporary, and we don't have time to help suppliers improve over the course of a single project."

"Our clients demand a transparent, low bid procurement approach, which prevents us from selecting the subcontractors and suppliers that we'd prefer to work with."

"The construction (or design or development) industry just doesn't work that way."

I say, "I don't buy it!"

The challenge of developing non-company people was the focus of an intense conversation I had with Gary, the president of a mid-sized general contracting firm that works primarily on hard bid (design-bid-build) public projects. Gary insisted that he did not have the ability to limit his use of subcontractors to only a few favored partners, and thus could not work to help any particular subcontractor improve over time. I asked which trades make up the majority of his subcontractors on a typical project. Gary confirmed that the mechanical and electrical trades usually perform nearly half of the subcontracted work. He added that if he included the structural contractors, masonry, and glazing trades, it would be closer to 70 percent. Then I asked him to list the companies that filled those roles on the last ten major projects completed by his company.

When he finished his list, Gary was surprised to see that it included only three HVAC contractors, two plumbers, and three glazing contractors. Further, one steel erector worked on seven of the ten projects, and a single masonry contractor worked on nine of ten. When I asked Gary again why he didn't regard some of these companies as partners, he was speechless. Suddenly the next step seemed obvious to him. Our conversation quickly switched from a discussion of why to how Gary could engage with these companies to develop them and their people to become partners in the success of his own company.

This perception of having little control over partner selection in project work is common. However, even when you can't select the trades yourself, the marketplace does a pretty good job of limiting your choices for any given element of the work. In Gary's situation, where subcontractors must be selected on a low bid basis, only a few qualified trades are available in each category in a given region, and only one or two specialize in a particular type of work. So, one electrician is most competitive on wastewater treatment projects, while another does best on mid-sized school projects, and yet another wins a significant percentage of the new fire station projects. We find the same trend for consultants such as electrical, mechanical, and structural engineers, acousticians, energy efficiency experts, lighting consultants, and landscape designers. The available choices are not as random and varied as we often think.

The situation gets even better for companies that work in the private sector under a more flexible procurement model. Because these companies can select subcontractors based on qualifications rather than price alone, they often weed out poorly performing subcontractors through a prequalification process and give special preference to companies with a strong track record. In that environment, it's common for general contractors and design firms to find a couple favorites that they turn to again and again in each category.

Consider what it would look like if you treated even a few of these subcontractors and suppliers (and the people who work for them) as an extension of your own firm. Could you find a way to help them improve, strengthen your relationship with them, and even rely on them the way you rely on your best long-term employees? The answer is a clear and strong "yes," and it's not as difficult or risky as you might think.

While I was a project manager working for a contractor on heavy industrial projects, our best client was an oil refinery in Minnesota that treated all of its turnaround contractors as partners. Turnarounds are short maintenance and upgrade projects that happen a few times each year and focus on one part of the overall refinery. They typically have a duration of eight to fifteen days. The shutdown costs the refinery millions of dollars each day in lost production, and it utilizes hundreds of boilermakers, pipefitters, electricians, scaffold erectors, and others working around the clock. My company provided boiler-maker labor and project management support for all the plant's turnarounds. This refinery—I'll call them MN Refining—engaged one or two companies for each category of work on a long-term basis, and paid for all work on a time-and-materials basis. Outsiders thought MN Refining was missing out on the benefit of competitive bidding and guaranteed pricing for each turnaround. What they didn't see was how these partners became integrated into the refinery's operations and saved the company millions each year in labor costs and downtime.

The last turnaround I worked on at MN Refining was the FCC (Fluid Catalytic Cracker) unit, the primary area of the plant where crude oil first enters the refining process. The FCC unit is the most critical part of an oil refinery and is only shut down every four years. When the FCC unit is shut down, it starves the rest of the refinery of incoming product, and one unit after another must be taken out of service as stores of incoming product are quickly used up. A lengthy FCC shutdown costs the refinery a fortune.

For this turnaround, we spent two years planning every detail of the work with MN Refining. Since our core staff, a handful of foremen, supervisors, engineers, and project managers, was on site year-round, even between turnarounds, we were able to work closely with the refinery operators, inspectors, and engineers to work out logistics, staging, and the tactics that we'd use to accomplish the work. The most challenging part of the project was to completely replace the internal components of the FCC reactor, a pressure vessel with three-inch thick steel walls measuring about sixteen feet in diameter and 120 feet tall. Our plan called for twelve days of intensive, around-the-clock work on the reactor, and all the other turnaround work was scheduled to fit within this same twelve-day schedule. Experts from our company were horrified when they learned that we had committed to such a short duration and insisted that we should allow at least sixteen days for the work. They didn't understand our relationship with MN Refining, or that we had worked out numerous special measures to allow us to work much faster than typical, including the bold step of allowing our own weld inspectors to have the final approval on all work. This eliminated the need for plant inspectors to do final weld checks and delay the next steps. Because we were partners, we were able to work out dozens of other special processes and contingencies that allowed us to work together in a streamlined way. Similar arrangements were made between MN Refining and all other contractors, as well as among the contractors themselves. In the end, we completed the FCC turnaround in exactly twelve days. It was a great victory for the team, but I didn't fully appreciate its significance until I got to my next project.

The following year, I was project manager erecting a series of oil storage tanks at a refinery in Wood River, Illinois, while the refinery was completing its own FCC turnaround. This refinery did not share MN Refining's belief in partnerships, but believed instead in the power of the hard bid process. They awarded the turnaround work to a single large contractor, one of our competitors, on a lump sum basis. Their contracted duration was about twenty days. Although not directly involved in the turnaround, I interacted daily with plant operators and inspectors as part of my tank project, and I got regular progress updates.

Through the contract language, the refinery did its best to put full responsibility for cost and schedule on the contractor's shoulders, a typical industry practice. In response, the contractor was forced to document every piece of work and make a claim for anything that was not included in the original scope. Replacing a corroded pipe spool, repairing a weld in one pressure vessel, or replacing a worn-out component in another all needed to be documented, priced, and approved before the work could be executed. There was no trust and little collaboration between the refinery and the contractor, and neither considered this a problem. The contract defined their obligations to each other, and both took actions to keep themselves whole. The same kind of relationship existed between the contractor and each subcontractor as well. As a result, work was often delayed while waiting for approvals, and the contractor had a small army of administrators on staff just to keep the paper river flowing as fast as possible. The project was completed with a final schedule of nearly forty days, at a cost that was about 60 percent higher than the original contract lump sum.

But the massive delays and overruns were not the biggest surprise. What shocked me the most was that no one was upset by the outcome. I expected the plant manager to be furious with the process and make bold statements about finding a better way to operate. Instead, he declared the project a marginal success. "These turnarounds are unpredictable. They always run longer than the original schedule and cost way more than the original price. It's just the nature of the work." In his world, the idea of partnering with contractors and achieving dramatically better results seemed not only impossible, it wasn't even on his radar.

Project work doesn't have to be like this. Whether you are a contractor, architect, engineer, or owner working in the project-driven world, you can take some practical measures to develop real partners who are integral to your company's growth and success.

First, change your thinking.

Recognize that an investment in these companies and their people is no different from an investment in your own people. They will almost certainly work for you again and again, and you will reap the rewards of their development along the way.

Many companies are concerned that helping their partners will end up benefiting their competitors as much as it helps their own company. After all, your competitors have access to the same pool of subcontractors, suppliers, and consultants that you do. There are several reasons why the risk is rarely realized. It's true that if your partners improve, it will almost certainly help your competitors a bit. This is unavoidable and it's not a bad thing. Raising the performance of any industry benefits its leaders most, and your company will be in the right position to take advantage of the gains. Second, your competitors, who are getting bits of improvement from individual subcontractors and suppliers, will not have the benefit of a coordinated, systematic approach to improvement that you are using with all your key partners. Their benefit will be diluted at best.

Finally, to your key partners, you will become their favorite general contractor (or owner, or designer, or developer) in each region where you work. These suppliers will recognize that they perform better on your projects and have a much better work experience when they work with you. In exchange for helping them improve, you will gain not only their trust and loyalty, but also their help when you need it, and most likely, preferential pricing over your competitors. You'll also achieve better performance on your projects, with fewer disputes, faster schedules, and the right level of quality the first time. Your investment in improving your key partners and their people will come back to you many times over.

Once you start thinking of your key contractors, consultants, or suppliers as partners, the process for developing them and their people should follow the same approach used for developing your own employees. Train them in your processes, challenge and empower them to work to their full potential, and expect them to make improvements along the way. Some key points to keep in mind while you do this are listed below.

Learn with Your Partners, Not Before Them

When we help our clients develop and apply lean improvements to their projects, they often want to refine and learn the new approach "in private," before trying to teach it to their partners. This view stems from a bias that their own company must be the leader and demonstrate competence before helping partners grow. However, learning in a silo presents two problems: First, it delays your partners' learning, something that we don't have time for in project work. Second, it results in improvements that impact only your company's people, sometimes even at the expense of your partners' work. Improvements that impact only a small segment of the work are ineffective in the project environment.

When companies develop and learn lean improvements together with their partners, they learn from each other and end up with better processes that take hold with the entire project team faster. Each project participant builds competency at an individual pace, and anyone who lags behind is supported by the team to overcome the inevitable challenges that arise when changing work habits. In addition, learning together builds trust and a sense of teamwork that you are in this together. It opens the door to greater transparency and honest feedback about what works and what doesn't.

When we reluctantly agree, despite our recommendations, to teach and coach our clients without including their key partners, there is one piece of feedback that we consistently get from participants:

"We should have followed your advice and included our partners from the beginning. It would have helped us work together so much better if we'd learned this together."

Ask Your Partners to Help Model New Habits

We've adopted a saying that's almost always true when teams learn new ways to work together: "Processes are easy to understand and change, but people are tricky." Too often companies think that changing work behavior is a matter of training, or even worse, sending out a memo that explains the new process. This will always end in failure. One client (against our recommendation) actually sent an all-company email that instructed people to trust each other more and argue less. You can imagine how little this impacted anyone's behavior.

If you intend to implement new processes for planning and managing work based on lean concepts, you'll likely have to bring many suppliers, contractors, or consultants along for the ride. To get real change in behaviors, consider asking one or two of your key partners to join you in the rollout. As your partners, they already understand why you are trying to make changes, and trust that you would not make a change unless it helped them as much as it helps you. In this environment, your partners can help model the new behaviors for the entire team and boost the speed at which the team adopts the change. This is surprisingly simple to do, and it has big benefits.

When we help companies implement the Last Planner® System, a lean planning and execution approach that I'll explain in a bit more detail in a later chapter, we often get them to implement the new processes with a few key partners right from the beginning. For example, the new system uses a specific method, called pull planning, to develop a coordinated plan for one phase of a project. The technique requires several companies working together to develop a shared plan of execution. It's a new way of thinking that requires a much higher level of collaboration, and that can make some people uncomfortable—afraid that they might be going out on a limb only to have it chopped off later. Explaining the process to one or two of your partners in advance and asking them to model the right behavior helps the rest of the team feel at ease. If this well-respected individual trusts you, others will take that as a sign that they can follow suit. Over time, this partner will become a valuable resource as you roll out the new processes on subsequent projects. If they vouch for the effectiveness of the Last Planner® System based on past experience, it carries a lot of credibility with other project participants—far more than you explaining the benefits yourself.

Practice Making Improvements Together

One of the best ways to develop your partners is to work on a specific improvement initiative together. This creates strong bonds between your companies and people, and provides immediate benefits for both organizations. It's best to think of these initiatives as small experiments that, if successful, can be replicated over time. I'll share more specifics about designing and running experiments in Chapter 6.

A good example of an improvement experiment is to minimize the amount of inventory that's lying around the jobsite, a common lean initiative in construction. The change removes a lot of clutter that can lead to unsafe working conditions, quality problems, and disruptions to workflow. Without a partnering mindset, companies might make declarations that only a certain amount of inventory will be allowed on the site, or that all materials must be kept on wheels so they can be easily moved when needed. The result is usually lukewarm participation from the team, and the need for "inventory police" to constantly patrol laydown areas and harp on those who are not falling in line with the program.

A much better approach is to work with one or two key partner companies that have the greatest need for stocking materials on site. Present the idea to them and work together to figure out what can be done to limit stockpiled inventory. You'll probably discover that they need the inventory because the work is unpredictable, and they often can't work where they need to on any given day. The inventory allows them the flexibility to grab stockpiled materials and keep their crews working, even when they have to work out of sequence.

To reduce the inventory of these partners, you'll have to first find a way to make the work more predictable. The partner companies will help you understand the problem (that is probably affecting everyone) and devise a couple ideas to make it better. If you can improve the predictability of the work together, reducing the inventory becomes simple. The learning can then be applied to the rest of the team, and the inventory reduction initiative becomes a success. The short experiment provides an opportunity for you to better understand your partners' work, and for them to understand some of the challenges you face. Your relationship and reliance on each other will be affirmed, and you'll improve your ability to work together to solve other problems. The result will be an improvement that benefits the entire project team and every future project, especially when it involves these partners.

Through these simple (and inexpensive) practices, you can begin developing your partners and their people, even though they are still only engaged intermittently on your projects. You will also be creating a change in culture and thinking in the people who work for you the most. I've witnessed this change in very tangible ways with many of our clients who undertake lean improvements. Over time, their partners begin to internalize the new behaviors and apply them to their work everywhere. On more than one occasion, we've seen clients' competitors scramble to try and emulate what they see happening on their suppliers' "favorite projects." Of course, these competitors cannot easily replicate your results. They are behind in the game and can only begin to catch up when they learn and internalize the changes required to get to breakthrough performance.

The question of whether to treat contractors like partners comes down to this: Are you happy with the results you're getting or do you want to lead the change to a better way of accomplishing project work? Once you've made the decision to change, building lasting relationships with true partners and bringing them along for the ride is a no-brainer.

———

5

Leading Without Authority

THE MODEL FOR LEADERSHIP in many industries is broken. In organizations that subscribe to traditional thinking, leaders are thought of as larger-than-life individuals who make the decisions, set the direction, and make sure everyone knows what to do and how to do it. They become the standards enforcers and the performance judges. They are the ones who intervene when things go wrong and save the day when others can't. What many organizations don't realize is that this type of leadership behavior and the culture in which it thrives also prevent individuals from taking on a higher level of accountability, making improvements to the way work gets done, and living up to their full potential.

Don't get me wrong, traditional leaders are not bad people. They are just stuck in an outdated environment and mindset that defines how they should behave as leaders. Their success is derived from their ability to work within the norms of that environment to achieve results. The "appropriate" leadership behavior has been modeled, learned, and rewarded over long periods of time at many levels.

The Leadership Behavior Matrix

Let me introduce a new way to think about leadership for the project-driven environment that is based on two characteristics of a leader's behavior—the extent to which a leader relies on their authority and the extent to which they demonstrate a respect for people. I'm intentionally talking about behavior here rather than a leader's thinking or philosophy. This is because a leader's behavior is what affects those around them and ultimately, their effectiveness as a leader. If a leader believes that their company needs to make big, aggressive changes to be successful, but repeatedly chooses the safe and conservative path for key decisions, their conservative behavior impacts the company while their aggressive philosophy does not.

While it's true that a leader's behavior is strongly influenced by their beliefs, it's also true that many other things can affect their behavior. We've all seen people who believe strongly in one thing but behave differently because culture, norms, outside pressure, and even formal company policies require something else. Can you think of a time when your own behavior did not align fully with your beliefs? My friend may believe that it's never OK to text while driving, but if he texts "just this one time" because he doesn't want his friends to wonder why he's not yet shown up for dinner, it's his behavior that causes a crash, not his beliefs.

In the following leadership behavior matrix, a leader's behavior is classified as "high" or "low" in each of two aspects: their reliance on authority and the degree to which they demonstrate respect for people. A leader's behavior in each aspect is independent of their level of seniority, position, or degree of formal authority over others. In fact, the behavior of every leader at every level of an organization can be defined along these two axes, whether we are describing a CEO or a crew leader on a building site. Before defining the labels in each quadrant, let's take a closer look at each axis.

Leadership Behavior Matrix

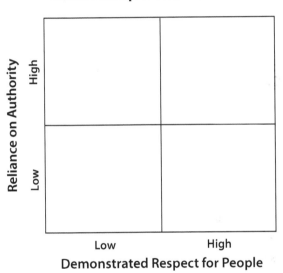

Reliance on Authority

The extent to which a leader relies on authority is different than the amount of actual authority they possess. A leader with lots of formal authority can elect to rely heavily on that authority to give orders and set goals unilaterally; or they could lead with a lighter touch, depending instead on building trust and giving a sense of autonomy to those who work for them. Likewise, a leader with little formal authority could push the limits of that authority to make demands and keep people in line; or they could work as a member of the team to raise performance through example and collaboration. Think about where you fit on this continuum, not by thinking about how you feel or what you believe is right, but based on past behavior. Do you have a preference for setting clear goals and holding people accountable? Or do you tend to solicit opinions from your people and work toward a collaborative solution? Most people find that they move between high and low reliance on authority, depending on the situation, but each has a comfort zone or a range that describes their behavior most of the time.

Level of Demonstrated Respect for People

The degree to which a leader demonstrates respect for people is indicated on the horizontal axis of the leadership behavior matrix. Respect for people is central to lean culture and is often misunderstood by outsiders. They think that respect for people is all about listening to people's ideas, empowering them to have a say in how the work should be done, and giving them personal autonomy in the workplace. These concepts are certainly part of the respect for people mindset but they miss an important element. To understand what's missing, take a moment to complete this simple exercise: write down the name of a person for whom you have great respect. It might be a teacher, boss, parent, coworker or friend. Now think about what you respect in this individual and about your relationship. With this person in mind, answer the question: If you respect someone, do you expect more from them or less?

The gap is now obvious. When you respect someone, you expect more from them. A lot more. You expect better ideas, more integrity, stronger performance, faster improvement, fewer errors, and seamless teamwork. So, when you solve problems for others—give them direction rather than autonomy, and limit their responsibility—you are demonstrating low respect for people, whether you respect them or not.

I've never met a person who says they don't have high respect for people, but the leadership matrix is measuring the extent to which a leader *demonstrates* respect for people, not what the leader believes. Then what does respect for people look like in behavior? Let's look at a comparison.

Low Demonstrated Respect for People	High Demonstrated Respect for People
Tell them what to do	Ask them what to do
Explain the problem	Let them to discover the problem
Set the goals	Teach them to set their own goals
Fix the problem for them	Let them struggle
Convince them of your way	Ask them to explain their way
Evaluate their performance	Ask them to evaluate your performance
Accept their results	Challenge them to do better
Expect little	Expect a lot

Having high respect for people is much simpler than actually *demonstrating* that respect consistently in your behavior. I've worked with many good people who have true concern for those they work with and for their growth and development. However, watching one of your direct reports struggle with a problem when you already know the answer is not easy. It requires a fixed belief that they will be better off in the long run if they figure this one out on their own. It also requires you to put the learning and growth of this individual ahead of the need for speed in solving the immediate problem. In addition, you have to consider the risk associated with the learning curve. Letting your child touch the hot stove might be the best way for them to learn about that hazard, but you would probably not let them play in traffic to learn the dangers of an oncoming bus.

Categorizing leadership behavior as high or low in each of these two elements provides four quadrants of leadership style. While no one is one-dimensional with a style described by only one label in the matrix, it's worth understanding what the behavior looks like in each quadrant.

Leadership Behavior Matrix

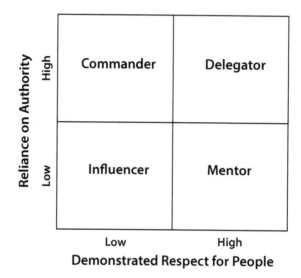

Commander

At the upper left corner of the matrix, commanders have the highest reliance on authority and lowest demonstrated respect for people of the four styles. They give orders and set expectations, passing mandates down the ranks. Usually operating under the preferred style of traditional top-down management, commanders require little input from their people and don't seek or desire a lot of feedback. They're expert at applying formal pressure to get people to work harder. Improvements usually come in response to past failures and result in added rules and requirements. They hold on to responsibility themselves to avoid being let down by others. A commander is a good boss if you like to stay in your own silo and do as you're told, but this approach limits the potential of those who work for them. If you are waiting for your boss to retire so you can get that next promotion, you probably work for a commander. Commanders often feel isolated and unsupported in their goals. They are fueled by personal accomplishment and achieving results. They get things done and are a valuable asset to their company, but they're stressed out and exhausted, feeling like they're fighting the same battles over and over again.

Influencer

Influencers are much like commanders, but act without authority. They get results by influencing others and use inspiration, coercion, or manipulation to make up for their lack of authority or discomfort in asserting it. They expect little feedback from their subordinates and primarily want to set a direction for others to follow. These leaders learn to get people to follow them even though they don't have to. Influencers can be effective at dealing with a commander boss by getting them to follow suggestions by convincing them that they came up with the idea themselves. Using political skill and charisma to inspire people, influencers can be fun to work with and are most likely to join the company bowling team and hang out after work. Influencers can get great results from their people, although their effectiveness can diminish over time as familiarity sets in. As influencers climb the ranks, they tend to rely more heavily on their newly acquired authority, often shifting toward the commander behavior over time.

Delegator

Delegators rely heavily on authority and recognize that their people are their greatest asset. They push much of their workload to subordinates while giving them little choice as to how they do it and little real responsibility. They make sure their people know exactly what's expected and follow up with tight oversight. These taskmasters know their success comes through their people, and do not hesitate to provide training and resources to help them succeed. A delegator can be exhausting to work for with the constant stream of tasks and assignments, but you will be rewarded with shared successes and a sense of personal accomplishment. Unlike commanders, delegators have high regard for the people they work with and are uncomfortable with the command and control culture in most organizations. Delegators who want to advance their careers are often forced by traditional organizations to shift toward a commander style of leadership, but they feel conflicted between the goal of developing their people and the push to get fast results. With maturity and experience, delegators sometimes make the shift toward a mentor leadership style, relying less on their authority and taking more responsibility for developing their people.

Mentor

Mentors lead with little authority and focus their energy on developing the people who work for them. Asking a lot of questions (even when they know the answer), these leaders expect people to work at a higher level and take on ever-increasing responsibility. In exchange, they take responsibility for advising, teaching, and coaching those who show an especially genuine interest in improving. A mentor encourages individuals to set aggressive goals for themselves and their team while ensuring they align with organizational objectives. This type of leader is a great boss if you're a self-starter who likes to push yourself to improve and learn new things, but can be frustrating if you just want to be told what to do. In traditional organizations, mentors are misunderstood as leaders who don't understand the pressures of modern business practices or the need for a firm hand. Given time,

102

mentors can achieve results that were once thought impossible, while their organizations often don't understand how it happened or give much credit to the mentor for making it possible. In lower management positions, mentors are often seen as agitators and idealists as they push for a model of managing people and developing capabilities that conflicts with traditional thinking. In top-level positions, mentors can transform companies into learning organizations that respond quickly to changing market conditions, and leverage their ability to improve as a strategic competitive advantage.

Defining a leader's behavior requires an acknowledgement that leaders behave differently in different situations, and that their typical behavior is best defined by a blended combination of the four quadrants. Think about where your own behavior fits in the model. While your beliefs may be consistent and unwavering, your behavior tends to be responsive to specific circumstances. Each person's leadership style is represented by a region in the matrix that shows their comfort zone—how they behave most of the time—their leadership behavior profile.

Traditional Leadership Behavior Profile

The shaded region in the matrix that follows indicates the behavior profile of what I'm calling traditional leaders who tend to rely heavily on authority and generally demonstrate low respect for people. These are the behaviors that are displayed by many of the people in positions of power and influence in many organizations today. It also represents the behavior of most people who work for them, emphasizing behaviors in their own leadership style that conform with traditional organizational structure, culture, and expectations.

Leadership Behavior Matrix

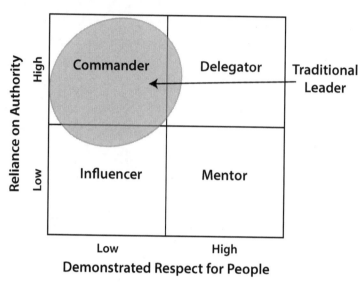

Reliance on Authority

High — Commander | Delegator — **Traditional Leader**

Low — Influencer | Mentor

Low   High

Demonstrated Respect for People

To understand the traditional leadership profile, consider a (partly) fictional story about a traditional leader, Peter, who was once a powerful executive with a long, successful career leading the construction operations at a large high-tech manufacturing company. While he was there, Peter's company was constantly upgrading, retooling, and expanding manufacturing facilities to the tune of billions of dollars annually. He had a staff of committed planners and managers who executed projects primarily through third-party designers, contractors, and suppliers. Because the company's ability to deliver new (and highly profitable) products was dependent on its ability to construct new manufacturing facilities faster than its competitors, Peter's department was critical to the overall success of the organization. This department is a typical project-driven organization within a larger company.

In the eyes of his company, Peter was an effective leader. He had a track record of delivering successful projects with ever-shorter schedules and tighter budgets. The projects grew exponentially more complex with each new technology release, and Peter was open to finding new ways to get the work done. He invested time and money in training his employees and teaching them new tactics for planning and managing construction work. He experimented with various contracting methods to get more from his contractors and suppliers. He set aggressive targets for schedules and budgets and was often able to get his people to achieve the goals.

Peter was blind to the fact that his people were responding primarily to his authority, and as a result, he was only tapping into part of his team's full potential. Using his authority, Peter turned up the heat on the pressure cooker that was each new project. Every subsequent initiative came with a shorter schedule and a tighter budget, which meant more stress, longer hours, and more pressure from above for everyone working in Peter's organization. While Peter's improvement initiatives were always met with enthusiasm on the surface, an undercurrent of discontent and frustration was obvious to everyone, except maybe Peter himself.

Peter earnestly tried to get his people to provide feedback and input, but the culture and his authoritative approach made it hard for anyone to tell him the honest truth. If Peter asked, "do you think we can really squeeze thirty days out of the schedule without risking quality?" the answer was almost always something like "it seems impossible, but we'll find a way if we have to." His people knew they could not say "no" and keep their job for very long.

Peter's style was a classic "management by objectives" approach— motivating people through pressure and ever-increasing goals over which the team had little or no influence. The organizational culture dissuaded individuals from speaking up which resulted in public approval and enthusiasm for the objectives along with private resentment. While on the surface it seemed that Peter's approach was popular and successful, it actually prevented leaders from hearing the truth, and prevented the full contribution of those who actually completed the work.

Peter learned the shortcomings of his approach only after taking an early retirement and going on to start his own consulting company. In this new role, Peter imagined he would leverage his reputation for results to help other companies achieve similar success. What he found was something quite different.

As a consultant, Peter no longer had authority over the people on his team. Without the authority of his position, Peter found that people were unconvinced by his ideas and unresponsive to his aggressive goals. Because he hadn't needed to in the past, Peter didn't understand how to build trust with his team, develop shared goals, or solicit real input as part of gaining the team's commitment to achieving big things. He had little understanding of how to mentor team members, elevate their capabilities, and make them part of setting goals, designing processes, and achieving results. His ability to use his authority to shortcut these steps in the past left him floundering when he found himself without his past authority to demand results at all cost.

Today, Peter is learning how to lead without authority and act more deliberately with regard to respect for people. He is finding this new style of leadership, and the culture that it creates, leads to an empowered workforce that is more deeply committed to the company's objectives, more capable of making improvements, and a much more effective force for dealing with the organization's biggest challenges, whatever they may be. He's also realizing how much more he could have accomplished at his old company, and how much better it would have been prepared for a challenging future if he had behaved this way in the first place. Today he recognizes how his "authority short-cuts" let him accomplish what was necessary while preventing him from achieving the full breadth of what was possible.

Peter's old traditional leadership style is typical in organizations of all kinds. In the project-driven environment, top-down traditional leadership and the inability to put respect for people into action handicap not only employees but contractors, consultants, and suppliers as well. First, leaders resort to motivation through intimidation and threats and impose their authority through a regimen of strict monitoring and enforcement. If suppliers have a hard time meeting schedules, the traditional leadership solution is to write tighter requirements into contracts and force contractors to provide weekly progress updates. If they are still falling behind, make them provide a corrective action plan showing how they'll get back on track. Threaten them with back charges and liquidated damages, and if they continue to struggle, threaten to terminate their contract. If needed, threaten to blacklist them from any opportunities to work on future projects.

These coercive measures accomplish the goal of turning up the heat on suppliers and subcontractors, and usually force them into compliance. However, this does nothing to help them understand the cause of their setbacks or take any steps to improve next time. While the approach may force them to meet the project requirements (barely), they will do so without learning anything and will be no better at partnering on the next project. Under the traditional leadership model, the idea that subcontractors and suppliers could ever become an asset to future projects is not even a consideration. By leveraging authority through this type of monitoring and enforcement, leaders are shortcutting the important and powerful work of leadership—developing these partners as an asset.

Whether applied to the companies or the people who complete the work, the traditional leadership behavior profile does little more than squeeze the most from existing capabilities. This behavior increases the pressure and pulls as much as possible from project participants while doing little or nothing to increase potential or raise performance levels.

Before I explain how to counter these traditional leadership habits in your own style, let's look at how a shift to an exponential leadership behavior profile impacts an organization over time.

Exponential Leadership Behavior Profile

The shaded region in the next matrix indicates the behavior of a different kind of leader. Whatever their position, these leaders rely much less on their authority and demonstrate a higher respect for people in their daily behavior. Their focus is on getting results by developing people to achieve their highest potential. They are rarely satisfied with the status quo and recognize that their own high expectations demand that they take more responsibility for supporting and coaching their people. They know that quick fixes and short-term results come at the expense of long-term capability, and they act in a way that heavily favors the latter. I call people with this leadership style exponential leaders. Through their behavior, they are building capability in others while multiplying their influence and effectiveness and, over time, creating a network of leaders by planting this leadership style and nurturing its growth. Along the way, they teach others to do the same in their own positions, thereby creating exponential growth in learning and development of leaders at every level. The result is a team of people in an organization that performs at a level that is unattainable with traditional leadership. These are the teams that achieve breakthroughs in every measure of project performance: safety, quality, cost, schedule, and innovation.

Leadership Behavior Matrix

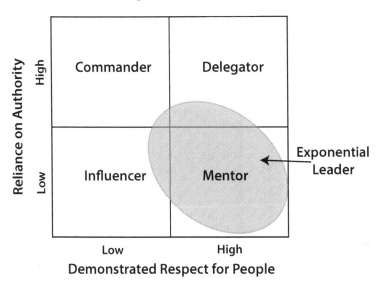

Exponential leadership is about developing capability and building an organization that can, above all else, grow and improve at a faster pace. The bad news is that building this capability takes some time, and people can only learn exponential leadership while practicing it in the real world. This means there will be a learning curve that can initially seem slow and unpredictable. The reason that many organizations fail to make the shift is because of the performance "lag" that sometimes occurs during the transition away from traditional leadership. This lag is illustrated in the next image, and although it is usually small and short-lived, organizations that demand short-term results within the confines of shortsighted metrics often don't have the patience to let the change take hold. The good news is that once exponential leadership behavior takes root, it becomes a powerful force for ongoing, ever-increasing rates of improvement into the future.

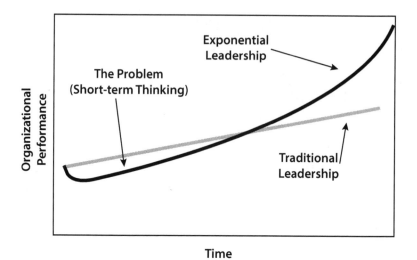

Time

Challenging leaders to have less reliance on authority and put a stronger emphasis on demonstrating respect for people through mentorship and coaching is no small request. It takes time and energy that many leaders believe they don't have. It takes skills that many leaders don't currently possess, like the ability to provide and receive honest feedback in a way that builds trust and opens the door for new levels of partnership. It requires a commitment to a new way of working which might seem unattainable at the onset. However, once they see that these behaviors align with their real concern for coworkers and create a space for growth and fulfillment while meeting the needs of the organization, leaders realize that they can begin to make the shift. As they continue to move toward an exponential leadership style, focusing on mentoring with little reliance on their authority, these leaders will find that they are creating a network of capability that makes it easier for their organization to respond to challenges and jump on new opportunities faster than their competition. It creates a cycle of improvement and growth that, over time, builds a culture of high performance, continuous improvement, and personal fulfillment.

Shifting from Traditional to Exponential Leadership

Though it might seem impossible to affect this kind of change in your organization, it starts by shifting your own behavior toward the exponential leadership profile. The shift is not as intimidating and difficult as it might seem. Don't think of this as a sudden move or some kind of disingenuous personality change. Instead, challenge yourself to learn new behaviors in small steps, and begin to replace your current leadership tactics with more effective ones. Here are some simple moves you can make to shift toward an exponential leadership style.

To create a shift toward the mentor role in the matrix, you must make it safe for your team to be open and honest. When you have trained people not to speak up, merely telling them that you value their opinion does not carry much weight. They've seen others' ideas get shot down, and probably had their own concerns ignored more than once. Even after an electric fence has been de-energized, the cows will still keep their distance. People are at least as smart.

One tactic that we often teach leaders who demonstrate traditional leadership habits is to lead with a focus on asking questions rather than directing. If you have a concern, train yourself to ask your people about it rather than tell them about it. The questioning should be done with the intention to uncover the deeper source of issues and create an environment where people are expected to bring problems up early, not bury them in hopes of staying out of trouble. This saves money and time by reducing cost overruns and delays that come when problems are ignored until they're in your face. It also provides an opportunity to support your people when they come to you with issues. To help understand this practice and the impact it can have, notice the difference in two conversations between the leader, Lynn, and her direct report, Tom.

111

Scenario 1

Lynn: Tom, I see in your status report that the engineering deliverables are expected to be late by two weeks. That would be catastrophic for our project, and we can't let that happen. I need you to get that back in line right away. Do I need to get your manager to jump in a take care of that for you, or can you make it happen?

Tom: No, I don't think that forecast is really as bad as it looks. I'll take care of it.

Scenario 2

Lynn: Tom, what's the status of that troubled engineering deliverable that you told me about last week?

Tom: Well, I'm projecting a two-week delay, which I know would be catastrophic. I'm afraid the reality might actually be worse than the projection.

Lynn: Yikes, what do you think is going on?

Tom: I'm pretty sure our engineering consultant has taken on more than they can handle. I've heard they have a crisis on another project that's pulling resources from this one.

Lynn: What do you think we can do about it?

Tom: I've asked our design lead, Paul, to speak to their manager to get to the bottom of it. He's supposed to let me know what he finds later this morning. He thinks he can get them to commit the right level of manpower to the work once they understand how critical that date is.

Lynn: Good. Can you give me an update after you hear from Paul?

Tom: Sure, at lunch today.

Lynn: Anything I can do to help?

Tom: If Paul can't get that commitment, I might need you to talk to their owner this afternoon. I know you have a good relationship with him.

Lynn: No problem, just let me know. I won't make that call until you say it's needed.

Tom: Thanks, see you at lunch.

In the first scenario, it's almost impossible for Tom to tell Lynn the truth. He's proud of his management abilities and he finds it hard to ask for help. He feels like it would be an admission of failure. Tom's stress level increases as a result of the conversation, and he goes back to work not knowing what to do next, and on top of that, dreading next week's update where he will have to admit to a three-week delay.

In the second scenario, Tom knows Lynn's leadership style and knows he'll be questioned about this issue. He comes to the discussion prepared and has already anticipated that Lynn will expect to hear his opinion and recommendations. Tom can be honest about the problem and knows that Lynn will help if he needs it. He anticipates the entire conversation and knows that asking for Paul's help is the obvious next step. He even makes that request before the meeting, and prepares Lynn for the potential that she'll have to step in. Lynn's leadership style allows for her team to manage these kinds of issues openly and brings the problem to light as soon as possible, allowing the team an opportunity to deal with it early while they still have a chance to avoid a crisis.

The shift required to change Lynn's behavior from the first to the second scenario above is subtle. She does not have to change her personality for it to be effective; she only needs to learn how to have different kinds of interactions with the people around her. The people working for Lynn might notice the shift and feel like Lynn has raised the bar a bit for what she expects from them. In practice, when a leader learns to interact in this way, it's only a short time before people notice a difference in the team. We often hear people describe the team as more cohesive, better at communicating, more open to feedback, and less defensive. It's surprising how often people attribute the change to something other than the leadership, saying, "it's a good group of people," or "they just seem to have gelled," or "everyone here contributes at a high level." The exponential leadership style is contagious and creates an environment where these behaviors are not only possible; they're expected.

When we coach leaders in this exponential leadership style, they mistakenly think this is about getting the same results with a "softer" approach. That's not the point. This approach allows for better outcomes that are not possible with the old approach. It can dramatically elevate the team and the leader's impact.

Another shift that leaders can make is to adopt behaviors that make their respect for people more obvious. A great exponential leadership technique is something called a gemba walk. Gemba is a Japanese term that means "the actual place." In project work, gemba is the place where value is added, where the actual work of the project is accomplished.

When leaders take a gemba walk they make the deliberate effort to visit the organization's front lines with the intent of understanding what is impacting the people. A good gemba walk focuses on asking questions, listening intently to concerns, challenging people to make improvements, making sincere offers to help when needed, and thanking individuals for their input. Exponential leaders incorporate gemba walks into their daily routines triggering an organization-wide shift in expectations and culture that leads to higher performance and faster improvements throughout the organization. Gemba walks demonstrate a leader's respect for people in a tangible way and break down the invisible barriers to communication that exist in many organizations. People who are approached during a gemba walk know that their opinion is valued and that they can influence the company's direction by adding their unique perspective. They are more connected to the overall goals and more likely to speak up when they see a problem.

A simple gemba walk can break through the isolation in which traditional leaders often feel trapped. If you haven't done this before, or if it's just been a long time since you connected with the people on your team, this can be an intimidating task. Traditional leaders don't know how to behave in this environment. They might feel out of place or like they are getting in the way of the work. Or they might sense that workers view them as an insurgent in their own organization, lurking among the workers to see what they're doing wrong. To overcome this barrier, be completely transparent about why you're there and what you're doing. When you approach someone at the gemba, open the conversation with "Hi, I'm Steve Smith, the manager of construction operations for the Chicago region of ABC Contractors. I'm here because I want to better understand the work of those delivering value to our customers, the people who actually do the work of building. Can you tell me about what you're doing?"

This disarming introduction can lead to a conversation that uncovers things you've never known before: problems with the current work processes, frustration with management, requests to make improvements that, until that moment, no one had uttered out loud. The entire interaction takes no more than a few minutes.

Conclude the interaction with "Thanks for letting me know about how things are going. I made a note about the problem with the battery life on the hammer drills and will bring it up to our procurement folks this afternoon. I really appreciate your honest feedback."

It's true that you have just taken responsibility to do something you haven't done in the past. You'll need to follow up with procurement and make sure that the front-line workers hear from them quickly. Your display of respect for people takes some commitment of time and energy.

You might feel like you never have time for this type of interaction, and can't imagine doing it daily. While you understand that *theoretically* you would be creating a better culture and empowering people at all levels of the organization to make it better, you might feel that you are stuck with the realities of the daily grind, the need to put out fires, and respond to more urgent issues. If so, you are living with the short-term problem shown in the last diagram, and you need to build your own capacity for this new behavior slowly, over time. The payoff will come when you spend less time putting out fires and have more time to do what's most important.

The solution is to take small, manageable steps while building your competence in this new behavior. Try having this type of interaction once a week, committing only thirty minutes each time. Make a point of taking a tour of the job site when you visit for a weekly meeting, or try walking through the cubicle farm where the designers are working. Do this deliberately and remember your objective—demonstrating and acting on your personal respect for people. You will be surprised by the positive impact it has on your organization and how it begins to change the behavior of leadership—yours and that of all leaders in the company. You will also notice an improvement in the flow of work in metrics like productivity, achievement of schedule milestones, and reduced rework.

Leadership is a tricky topic. Many companies struggle with defining what's expected of their leaders, and few people are ever taught how to lead effectively. The model of exponential leadership provides a way for you to shift your leadership style toward the behaviors that have the biggest impact on your organization's long-term improvement and growth. It provides a model that you can teach to others and a way to develop a consistent leadership approach across all levels of your organization. By looking at behaviors rather than beliefs, you can understand your own style and how it impacts those around you. Once you start on the path toward exponential leadership, you are on your way to unlocking the power of everyone in your organization and creating a network of leaders that power your learning organization.

———

6

Learn Through Fearless Experimentation

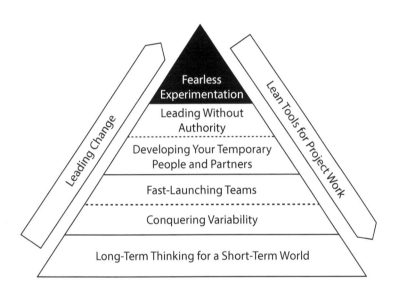

IN LEAN THINKING, THE ultimate goal is to create a true learning organization—one where "People continuously expand their capacity to create the results they truly desire, where new and expansive patterns of thinking are nurtured, where collaborative aspiration is set free, and where people are continuously learning how to learn together."[17] This objective is a lofty one, and even best-in-class lean companies like Toyota will tell you they are still moving on the path toward it, with a long way to go. But the spirit of this mission creates

---

[17] Peter M. Senge, *The Fifth Discipline: The Art & Practice of the Learning Organization* (New York: Doubleday, 1990); Jeffrey K. Liker, The Toyota Way: 14 Management Principles from the World's Greatest Manufacturer (New York: McGraw-Hill Education, 2004)

a mindset of optimism and opportunity, of challenge and obligation, that drives the organization and its people to continuously strive for something more.

The ability to learn makes everything else in the Better Building model possible. It is the meta-skill that allows for the development of all other skills. Learning *how to learn*, both as individuals and as an organization, is the primary strategic advantage that allows lean companies to consistently outperform their competition. In the project-driven organization, the ability to learn is what allows for better outcomes in every measure—delivering projects faster and at a lower cost, creating a safer work environment with fewer injuries and accidents, achieving consistent quality with shorter punch lists and fewer callbacks, and creating a more enjoyable experience for clients, partners, and your team.

However, this ability to learn must be deliberately created, nurtured, and strengthened in a way that weaves it into the fabric of the organization. Many companies try to emulate Toyota's learning culture by adopting its problem-solving techniques rather than adopting its learning culture. While lean tools like 5-Whys Root Cause Analysis and A3 Problem-Solving[18] can be very effective, their effectiveness at Toyota comes from the development and creation of the tools to suit the environment in which they are used. Because Toyota developed these tools to fit their culture and specific way of learning, they provide great results; but blindly copying these kinds of tools will not lead your organization to the same kind of results.

To get the best results for your organization, think instead about how your own improvement tools and culture can be developed to fit your environment and make learning a way of life. This type of organizational learning, growth, and improvement requires a

---

[18] These and other lean tools are described briefly in Chapter 8.

sense of adventure and exploration that is absent in most of the project-driven organizations I've run across in my years in the building industry. What's missing is what I call a spirit of "fearless experimentation"—an organizational approach to improvement that builds learning capacity in individuals, teams, and the organization as a whole. Before tackling the specifics of learning through fearless experimentation, it's worth understanding how we learn as human beings.

At the most fundamental level, humans learn through observation and trial and error. As infants, we observe what's happening around us and mimic what we see and hear. A child learns language by copying what they hear around them. Utterances that get a positive response are repeated, and those that don't are left behind as we learn how to best communicate with those around us.

As we get older, we are exposed to learning by instruction. This is accomplished through listening to teachers, reading books, and watching presentations. This model treats learning not as discovery or invention, but as a transfer of knowledge. The institutions that most of us attended from kindergarten through high school, college, and even into our professional careers utilize this one-to-many style of instruction to teach skills and convey information, not because it is more effective for the individual learner, but because it allows for a large number of individuals to learn from a single teacher. Julia Child taught thousands of aspiring chefs through her television shows and books, but where do you think you'd learn more: through a year of one-to-many teaching opportunities or by spending a single week with Julia in your kitchen? We've learned to accept this less than ideal learning process because of the limited number of teachers, the expense of personal learning, and our view of learning as merely the transfer of knowledge.

For scientists, learning is not primarily a matter of transferring knowledge, but a search for new understanding or discovery. This type of learning is accomplished through what is known as the scientific method, which relies on a repeatable cycle of prediction, experimentation, and observation to learn new things. The scientific method starts with observation and the formulation of a question: "Why do my new houseplants die within two months?" The question causes the formulation of a hypothesis: "My houseplants die because they don't get enough water." The hypothesis allows one to formulate a prediction: "If I water my plants they will not die." Next, the prediction is tested through one or more experiments: I water my plants each week for two months. Finally, observation lets us evaluate the results of the experiment and determine if the underlying hypothesis is correct or incorrect. Since I watered my plants once a week for two months, and they all died, my hypothesis must be incorrect. It must be something other than a lack of water that's killing my plants. The conclusion leads to new questions and new hypotheses that can be tested with a different experiment: "Maybe they need more sunlight."

This scientific approach to discovery, invention, and learning adds structure to our instinctive observations, and trial-and-error learning, so that it can be repeated and shared with others. By sharing not only the outcomes, but also the methods and processes, scientists save others from pursuing the same incorrect hypotheses in the future and accelerate the pace of discovery within the community. The speed of discovery increases as more concurrent experiments are conducted to test multiple hypotheses; and the community gains ever-increasing understanding of the underlying phenomenon with every iteration.

The idea of fearless experimentation is built on a spirit of learning and continuous improvement through the scientific method of experimentation. But it's not just about the experiments. Imagine if a company hired a team of experimenters or improvement experts—people whose only job was to improve the organization and its processes. A team like this could become quite efficient at designing and conducting experiments and then developing improvements to processes that would positively impact the entire company. Although the experts might develop legitimate process improvements, the changes may not be embraced by the rest of the organization and would not automatically have the commitment of every individual to ensure they are successful.

While making improvements is important, it is only when everyone in the company is engaged in and responsible for improvement that it becomes an integral organizational skill that's built into the culture. Lean companies understand that experimentation and learning are only effective when they're done at all levels by the people responsible for the work. When everyone seeks to learn in an effort to make improvements all the time, then it is truly a learning organization.

This is important because the most impactful discovery is the one we make ourselves. A wise friend once told me that if you share a new idea with someone, they typically receive it in one of two ways. Either the idea is considered trivial: "I know that already," or utopian: "That idea is impossible to implement and too good to be true." Fearless experimentation provides an approach to organizational learning and improvement through distributed experiments—conducted at all levels of the organization by the people working there. Learning through fearless experimentation has three parallel objectives: first, it is about improving everything that an organization does; second, it's about building its internal learning capability; and finally, it must be done without creating undue risk for the people, the project, or the organization. The outcomes are not sequential or built one on the other, they happen at the same time. This mindset of fearless experimentation not only creates improvements for the organization in a safe environment but also increases the capacity for learning and improvement along the way. The process of fearless experimentation is based on the following elements:

1. Set Powerful Objectives
2. Use Short Learning Cycles
3. Learn on Value-Added Work
4. Control the Risk
5. Experiment at All Levels

Set Powerful Objectives

A potential client once called us for help "training his people about lean construction" on one of the company's largest projects ever—the design and construction of a long-span suspension bridge with a lump sum contract amount approaching two billion dollars. I asked what they were hoping to accomplish with the training, and he replied that he wanted his crews to use lean concepts to deliver the project. This seemed to me like a pretty weak objective so I asked a more direct question "What do you expect to be different after your people learn about lean?" He didn't have an answer. This company was chasing the idea of lean construction without thinking seriously about why. We see this type of ill-fated attempt at lean improvement often, and without a compelling purpose (a powerful objective), virtually no initiative will succeed.

To help our clients formulate powerful objectives—those that will lead to tangible, repeatable benefits—we spend time with leadership and team members trying to understand the risks and opportunities of any given project or initiative. By summarizing the key project information and the current state of the organization, we can begin to understand which objectives might be most valuable to the project and the organization. For the company facing the large bridge project we discovered the following key information:

- The project includes heavy penalties for late completion.

- The lump sum contract means that any costs savings will directly increase the company profit and overruns will decrease it.

- A large portion of the design, fabrication, and erection work will be completed by internal resources, so much of the risk (and reward) lies within their own company.

- The project uses a structural system that is unfamiliar to the company and the client.

- The project has a three-year construction schedule in a location where lots of time could be lost during the rainy season each spring.

After reviewing the risks and opportunities, we were able to define the objective in a way that is much more valuable to the company than just learning to apply lean techniques. We encouraged the company to try a series of experiments with this objective:

Apply lean thinking to the design and construction of the project to develop effective methods for constructing the new structural system, reduce labor costs by 10 percent, and reduce the construction schedule by four months, thereby reducing the risk of late completion and eliminating an entire season of work during rainy spring months. Through the process, learn how to apply similar thinking to all projects across the entire company.

It's easy to see how formulating specific, clear, and powerful objectives provides the focus and motivation to make real improvements that have measurable impacts on success for the project and benefits to the bottom line. At the start of such an initiative, our clients usually have no idea how they will accomplish such challenging goals, but we know from experience that these types of powerful objectives provide the motivation and focus required to get team members engaged so that they learn and improve as an organization, and align the efforts of the entire project team with the company.

To be powerful, an improvement or learning objective, whether for a shift in behavior of an entire company or for the results on a single project, must include several elements. First, the objective must be specific enough to allow you to establish metrics that let you know if you are achieving the objective or not. For the sample objective above, each experiment would establish metrics that verify the objective is being met along the way. Are we saving 10 percent of labor costs? Are we reducing the time frame to save four months of construction time?

Second, the objective must strike a balance between challenge and achievability. An overly simple objective does not inspire people to make a change because it allows them to believe that their current practices will get them there. An impossible objective leaves people feeling hopeless. When effective, an improvement objective acts as a call to arms for the people who will be responsible to achieve it, taking them out of their comfort zone enough to try something new while not paralyzing them with fear of failure. As the learning capabilities of individuals and the organization continue to develop, you'll find that goals can become more aggressive, and the appetite for challenge in the team grows quickly.

Finally, the objective must provide tangible benefit to the organization and its people. Imagine breaking down the elements of the sample objective above. What will it mean for the company and its people if we can invent improved methods for constructing the new structural system? What does it look like to finish four months early? How much profit is generated by a 10 percent reduction in labor savings, and how does it affect workers' bonuses? How would our learning on this project benefit other projects and the company as a whole? The answers are not explicitly provided in the objective, but the connections are easy to make. As teams begin working to meet the objectives, they can break them down to further define the outcomes and paint a vivid picture of what success looks like.

Setting valuable objectives is only the first step in using fearless experimentation as a learning and improvement process, but it is a critical one. Make the effort to get it right and your learning journey will be off to the right start.

Use Short Learning Cycles

The PDCA process has been at the heart of continuous improvement for decades in the United States and around the world. The steps: *Plan—Do—Check—Act*, create a cycle that allows for processes to be improved quickly and continuously and has been applied to every industry—from manufacturing to banking to healthcare to design and construction. The mistake that many project-driven organizations make when applying the PDCA cycle is to think of it as a cycle that happens once on every project. They plan the work, complete the project, and then conduct a "post-mortem" evaluation of their performance. Depending on the project, this PDCA cycle could take months or years to complete, thereby having no improvement effect on the current project, and leaving the team with stale information when thinking about what to improve for the next project.

To get the most from the PDCA learning cycle, it's important to make it as short as possible. Instead of running the cycle once on a project, we often set up weekly or even daily PDCA loops within a single project or across several projects at the same time. In the context of fearless experimentation, this means that each experiment must be designed as a series of experiments that provide quick feedback to the team so they can make adjustments and try again immediately.

A good example of this type of short-cycle experimentation happened on the construction of a five-story apartment building. The general contractor had struggled on past projects to complete on time without spending a fortune on overtime. They also realized that the end-of-project rush led to quality issues, expensive rework, and customers who were not satisfied with the building process. It's common for projects like this to spend tens of thousands of dollars in overtime in the last few weeks of work and to complete punch list repairs for weeks after the project is technically complete.

The experiment's objective was to create smoother, more predictable work flow and reduce their typical project schedule by one month while eliminating all overtime work that typically happened at the end of a project. They designed an experiment to divide the work into small batches and get the trades to follow each other through the building in a way that was much more predictable than their typical workflow. The experiment required each trade to complete a block of twelve apartments every five days so that the painting would be followed by the flooring, casework, countertops, wall tile, and finally, the electrical and plumbing trim work. Each trade had exactly five days to do their work and move to the next batch of twelve apartments.

Because the batches were small and the duration was only five days from one trade to the next, the team had almost immediate feedback about what was working and what wasn't. The wall tile contractor was only on site for three days before everyone realized that they were falling behind the five-day pace. By the end of the first week on the job, the tile contractor increased their crew size and learned to complete a twelve-apartment batch in the required five-day time slot. The short learning cycle provided quick feedback to the team and allowed for a timely adjustment to the work approach.

After another three weeks, the team realized that it might be possible to reduce the cycle time from five days to four for every trade. If achieved, this would cut an additional three weeks off the remaining five months of construction schedule. They agreed to try it. The following week, they discovered which two trades were struggling with the shorter cycle and helped them adjust by changing crew size, changing their material flow, or adjusting the sequence of work. After two weeks of this fine-tuning, the entire project was running smoothly on the four-day pace. The short learning cycle allowed for immediate feedback, quick adjustments, and rapid improvement across the entire project team.

Afterward, the project superintendent told me this was the smoothest project he had ever completed, and it had required virtually no overtime to finish comfortably ahead of schedule. He said that he would use the small batch approach on every one of his projects going forward. The experiment not only changed his thinking, it has injected the rest of the company with a new zeal for making improvements through experimentation.

Learn on Value-Added Work

The term "value-added work" refers to the core part of your business—the work that your customers pay you for because it solves their need. While there are many components to your business that are necessary for it to function, the value-added work is the reason that you are in business in the first place. To understand what part of your business delivers value to your clients, think of value-added work as that which creates a transformation, in materials or information, to provide something that your customer is willing to pay for. On construction projects, the value-added work includes placing concrete, erecting steel, driving nails, and installing tile. In engineering, the value-added work could include making calculations, interpreting design requirements, or creating production drawings. While procurement, HR, accounting, quality assurance, and safety functions are important and even essential to your business, these are not the value-added functions of your organization and not what you are in business to provide your customers.

Too often, project-driven companies learning to apply lean thinking to their operations want to start with improvement initiatives that target the wrong thing. Rather than focusing on the value-added part of their operations, they try to improve administrative processes that are secondary to their core business. They put great effort into improving their processes for paying invoices, writing proposals, or generating reports. These may be important, but they are not what their clients are paying for or where they bring the most expertise to the process.

A much better place to start is with the core operations of the organization, the value-added work that you are in business to provide to your customers. Only by improving these core functions will you increase the value that you provide customers and strengthen your competitive position. This can be an especially challenging proposal in project-driven organizations because so much of the work is accomplished by subcontractors and consultants—third party organizations over which you do not have complete control. I'm convinced that this is why many project-driven organizations avoid attempting serious learning on their value-added work and choose to focus on internal (non value-added) processes instead. I'm also convinced that learning to improve your value-added work provides the most benefit for your customers and is the most powerful strategic advantage for your company.

To find targets for experimentation on value-added work, start at the place where the core work of your business happens. You will not see it from your office or the project trailer on a construction site. Talk to the people doing the work and ask what bugs them about their daily process. You will probably discover that welders are frustrated by long setup times and other trades stockpiling materials in their work areas. Engineers are frustrated by the late or inconclusive decisions from the clients. Architects are annoyed when they have to redesign a building layout multiple times because the information about mechanical equipment is inaccurate or incomplete. Carpenters hate delaying a concrete pour because the steel embeds are always placed at the last minute and often in the wrong place. These are the parts of your value-added work that are screaming for improvement.

Unfortunately, even the simplest processes can become complicated in project-driven work. Getting the work area cleared for the welder may require the coordination of a dozen trades and planning to a level of detail that you've never been able to achieve before. Don't be discouraged and don't feel like you have to solve the whole problem in one shot. Because you are working on the value-added work, even a small improvement will have a direct benefit to your customer and your organization. Set a powerful objective, like helping the welder reduce setup time by 10 percent, and design a short learning cycle, like checking back in two days to see if the changes are having the desired impact. By starting with even the smallest experiment on value-added work, you will be building learning capacity where it is most powerful and most influential for your organization's bottom line. The small experiments and early successes will build confidence in the team and allow for more challenging experiments and improvement in the future.

By aiming your learning efforts at value-added work, you are sending a signal to the entire organization that this is the real deal. We are up to improving the heart of our organization and chasing improvements that will directly impact our customers and our bottom line. Avoid "big wins" on trivial, non value-added work in favor of small wins on the important stuff. You will ignite the spirit of experimentation where it matters most.

Control the Risk

To have fearless experimentation, you first have to eliminate the fear. There are two kinds of fear that get in the way of experimentation. First, there is fear of organizational risk, like risking project outcomes or profitability in pursuit of improvement. Second, there is fear of personal risk, like the fear of looking incompetent or naively optimistic. This is challenging when people are learning something new as they truly are not yet competent. Eliminating risk is about dealing with both the organizational and personal risks that hinder a spirit of experimentation. First, let's deal with the organization and the commercial risk.

Organizations are often afraid to learn how to improve their value-added work because the stakes are so high. It would be discouraging to try to improve a critical part of your business only to find that you don't yet know how to do it. It would be even worse to get hung up on an improvement effort only to disrupt the company's workflow and miss a deadline, or create some kind of quality problem with your key work process. These risks are real, and you must design experiments to be safe—not risking your business outcomes in the interest of improvement.

We worked with a high-tech manufacturing company that was trying to increase the speed of installing equipment required to get new products to market. Each piece of equipment was its own mini-project with an installation duration of about forty-five days. There were hundreds of pieces of equipment on the overall project.

To create a risk-free experimentation environment, we tried to reduce the duration and labor costs for just a single piece of equipment. The team, consisting of a general contractor, five trade contractors, a design engineer, and an owner's representative, developed a plan to complete the installation in thirty-three days. The shorter schedule allowed the installation to begin twelve days later than scheduled and still finish on time—a shift that would allow for more thorough design and complete procurement of materials in advance of construction. The reduction in schedule and manpower, if applied to all equipment on the project, would allow the new product to be delivered to the market on time (a feat which was in jeopardy before this experiment) and save millions of dollars in labor costs. However, the team was reluctant to commit to such a dramatic improvement for fear of creating unrealistic expectations or even worse, making changes that would actually cause them to slow down. If the overall project fell behind as a result of this experiment, it would be impossible, or at least very expensive, to catch up later.

The solution was to design a short-cycle, limited risk experiment on one pilot piece of equipment. The team decided to stick with the thirty-three day plan, but only count on achieving half the expected time-savings. As a result, they agreed to start the installation six days later than scheduled and complete it six days earlier than scheduled. Still getting a total time-savings of twelve days, but at a greatly reduced the risk of finishing late.

The first installation completed in thirty-seven days, a savings of eight (not twelve) days from the originally allotted time frame. Even with the six-day delay in start of work, the equipment was still finished two days ahead of schedule. The team did not meet their goal of saving twelve days, but also did not put the project at risk. On future equipment, the team continued to experiment and learn how to further reduce durations and labor costs. As the project progressed, they eventually developed practices that enabled them to consistently install equipment in thirty-three days. The new product was delivered to the customer on time, and the project realized a significant labor savings.

Personal fear is harder to eliminate than commercial risk. There are many reasons why individuals are afraid to stick their necks out or try something new, but one of the biggest barriers is the fear of looking like a beginner or like you don't know what you are doing. Of course, in every experiment the outcome is uncertain, otherwise the experiment would be unnecessary in the first place, and experimenters are always beginners in what they are trying to learn.

To reduce this personal fear of failure, we teach individuals to encourage and embrace the process of learning as an adventure. Think of what you don't know not as a shortcoming or failure, but as an opportunity to improve yourself and your organization. By accepting that you are a learner, you remove the stigma of not knowing and create an opportunity to enjoy the learning process. Peter J. Denning, professor of computer science at the Naval Postgraduate School, understands that his students are sometimes intimidated by the process of learning something new. Rather than viewing these times as failure, he wants his students to embrace the process of learning as an opportunity and maybe an exciting adventure. To help his students adopt a positive learning mindset, he asks them to read and reread his Beginner's Creed.

The Beginner's Creed

I am a beginner.

I am entering a new game about which I know nothing.

I do not yet know how to move in this game.

I see many other people playing in this game now.

This game has gone on for many years prior to my arrival.

I am a new recruit arriving here for the first time.

I see value to me in learning to navigate in this domain.

There is much for me to learn:

The basic terminology

The basic rules

The basic moves of action

The basic strategies

While I am learning these things I may feel various negative reactions:

Overwhelmed at how much there is to learn

Insecure that I do not know what to do

Inadequate that I lack the capacity to do this

Frustrated and discouraged that my progress is so slow

Angry that I have been given insufficient guidance

Anxious that I will never perform up to expectations on which my career depends

Embarrassed that everyone can see my mistakes

But these moods are part of being a beginner. It does not serve my goal and ambition to dwell in them. Instead,

If I make a mistake, I will ask what lesson does this teach.

If I make a discovery, I will celebrate my aha! moment.

If I feel alone, I will remember that I have many friends ready to help.

If I am stuck, I will ask for help from my teachers.

Over time, I will make fewer mistakes.

I will gain confidence in my abilities.

I will need less guidance from my teachers and friends.

I will gain familiarity with the game.

I will be able to have intelligent conversations with others in the game.

I will not cause breakdowns for promises that I lack the competence to keep.

I have an ambition to become competent, perhaps even proficient or expert in this game. But for now,

I am a beginner.[19]

The beginner's creed is a great way to remove the personal fear and discomfort that come with learning in public. In organizations, unlike in the classroom, it's up to the leaders to create an environment where learning and the necessary mistakes are accepted and even expected. This starts when leaders become part of the experiments and part of the inevitable failures. When an organization celebrates those who are beginners and any experiments that fail as part of the learning process, the culture learns to value the learning. By admitting that we are all beginners in some realm, even the top bosses are beginners at something, leaders get to model fearless experimentation to the point that it becomes the norm within the organization, and eventually is adopted at every level.

Minimizing the commercial risk and removing the personal fear from experiments allow them to become more public, and learning to become part of everyone's job. Unless both these barriers are addressed head on, the power of experimentation will never be fully realized.

---

[19] Gloria P. Flores, *Learning to Learn and the Navigation of Moods: The Meta-Skill for the Acquisition of Skills* (n.p.: Pluralistic Networks Publishing, 2016)

Experiment at All Levels

To be truly effective, experimentation and learning must happen at all levels and not thought of as the work of management alone. This means that leaders at every level have to learn to teach fearless experimentation to those who work for them. It will look different at each level.

At the work face, a fearless experiment might take the form of one individual improving the task he's responsible for. One of our clients set up a "quick and easy" improvement process to encourage and recognize workers who experimented and made improvements. Within this culture I witnessed individuals, mostly carpenters and laborers, conducting experiments and making improvements to their daily work.

One laborer was frustrated by the tedious process of removing snow from fluted metal decks before placing rebar and pouring concrete, a process that's frequently required during a typical Minnesota winter. Their current process included removing the snow with rotating power brushes and following up with leaf blowers to clear snow from the flutes that was left behind by the brushes. It took three workers at least half a day for a typical-sized deck pour as they power brushed the deck, blew out the flutes, and went over it again to clean up the dust that was left behind by the blowers.

This laborer devised an experiment. He predicted that if he cut the brush head to match the profile of the fluted deck, he could clear all the snow in one pass and eliminate the need for blowers altogether. The experiment cost him about two hours of his time and the "butchering" of a $400 brush head. At the first snowfall, the worker was able to single-handedly clear the snow in about two hours. The company quickly replicated the new brush design to make it available for their crews' other projects. A process that the company had struggled with for decades was greatly improved because one individual was allowed (and expected) to experiment and make improvements.

At the management level, an experiment may take a different tact. We worked with a contractor who was having great difficulty getting the designer to respond to requests for information (RFIs) in a timely manner. The designer seemed to ignore the urgency of many of these requests and disregard the impact they were having on construction progress. The team invited the designer to attend their weekly coordination meeting, but he refused stating that he only budgeted time to attend a single meeting each week—the Owner/Architect/Contractor (OAC) meeting. Frustrated by the lack of response and recognizing that the project was headed for failure if something didn't change quickly, the project team devised an experiment.

They agreed to prioritize the RFIs in order of urgency and provide the list each week to the designer. This would allow him to focus on the most critical RFIs, and keep the work in the field moving with much less delay. It took the team only one week to realize that their experiment failed. The prioritization was valuable, but there was so much noise and chaos on the project that the designer was still not paying attention to the most critical RFIs.

They modified the experiment the second week. Instead of providing the prioritized list by email, the team decided to create it together on a whiteboard during their weekly coordination meeting. Although the design team did not attend this meeting, it was held in the same room as the weekly OAC meeting. The whiteboard was strategically placed on the wall directly across from the spot where the designer typically sat at the OAC meeting.

At the next OAC meeting, even before the contractor had a chance to introduce the prioritized RFI list, the designer was immediately drawn to the whiteboard. "What is this list?" he asked. "Are these the same RFI's in the log that's emailed to us each week? What's the significance of the order and the highlighting?" The conversation went on from there, and the contractor and designer agreed that this list would be reviewed as the first agenda item at the OAC meeting. The designer appreciated the prioritization as it allowed him to focus on critical RFIs while setting others aside for later. The contractor and the entire construction team knew that if an RFI was given top priority, it would be answered without delay.

The spirit of experimentation created an immediate improvement on that project and taught all the organizations how to improve project-level communications. The approach they came up with for sharing high priority information has been broadly adopted and further improved by the contractor, the owner, and designer and is used on other projects. Fearless experimentation is not a process, but a mindset. It's built on the five elements explained in this chapter and has the parallel objectives of making specific improvements while developing the organization's capacity for learning and improvement. Do this in a way that minimizes risk to the organization and individuals, and you are on the path to becoming a true learning organization.

7

Leading Change

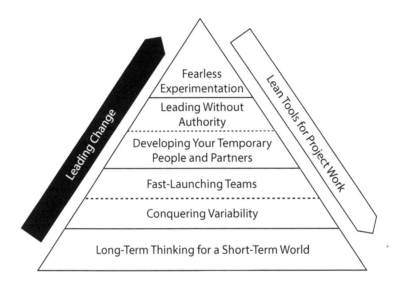

WHETHER THEY KNOW IT or not, every company that contacts us for help with lean is on a journey—one that will be defined by their ability to lead change. While a common initial request is often for help applying a lean tool or technique, we know that the successful implementation of even the most basic lean tactic requires the ability to cause a fundamental change in the behavior of people, most often starting with the leaders' ability to change themselves. Much more than any lean process or practice, this ability to shift behavior is the engine that powers every successful lean transformation.

As we guide our clients through this transformation, we first stress that change will not happen overnight. Allowing time for change is not only OK, it's necessary. It's often harder to unlearn old habits and paradigms than it is to learn new ones, and learning to apply a new way of thinking takes a new level of understanding that comes only through practice and implementation. Fortunately, many rewards are achieved along the way, rather than at the crossing of some artificial finish line. Each new capability leads to a deeper understanding that provides a new basis for further improvement. In a lean transformation, the journey is the reward.

The Better Building model offers a powerful new lens through which to view the project-driven organization; a paradigm that challenges the traditional way of thinking about work, learning, leadership, and what it takes to build a successful organization. Whether you're applying this new thinking to your immediate team or an entire enterprise, making the move from where you are to where you want to be can be intimidating. It doesn't have to be. This chapter describes some proven techniques that we use with clients as they learn to lead change—both in themselves and within their organizations.

The "Leading Change" arrow in the Better Building model represents the process of adopting a new mindset that begins with strategy and flows upward through the organization, with the ultimate objective of improving how the organization achieves its value-added work. As each element of the model is learned and practiced, it is up to leadership at every level to provide the direction and energy required to make a successful transformation.

This is about leading and not just managing change. The difference is critical. Change for the sake of change, without purposeful direction, can cause an organization to flounder as it chases one fad after another. Over time, this rudderless approach ends with little forward progress and a general mood of disinterest, apathy, and frustration. Managing rather than leading this type of change will not fix the fundamental problem of a lack of direction and purpose. Following the "change leadership" principles outlined here will help you avoid these mistakes and quickly get you headed in the right direction.

The change leadership approach we instill in our clients is not a "five-step process" or predetermined road map. Rather, we teach companies to rely on a few key principles that steer the actions of leaders at all levels. These principles create positive momentum toward new behaviors and new thinking while overcoming many of the barriers to change that keep people and organizations rooted in old habits. Adopting change is not just a matter of adding new tools to your existing toolbox. It requires you to eliminate old thinking and practices and exchange them for a new mindset. These five principles help leaders deal with the biggest challenges in change leadership.

Principles for Leading Change:
1. Know Where You Are
2. Set Clear Goals
3. Expect Resistance
4. Practice Leadership at Every Level
5. Change Routines to Change Thinking

Know Where You Are

When I was just getting my feet wet in the consulting business, I was visiting two new clients in the same week with one of my partners, John. One client was a large general contractor headquartered in Des Moines, and the other was the premier healthcare provider in Cleveland. John and I were walking one evening in search of a restaurant that was north of our hotel along the riverwalk. I remarked that the river must flow into the lake, so north must be downstream. I had lived close to Lake Michigan for years and was used to thinking of the large body of water and its tributaries as a navigational guide. In this case, my sense of direction in this unfamiliar city was anchored in the understanding that Cleveland was on the south shore of Lake Erie, and the knowledge that rivers flow into, not out of, the Great Lakes. John gave me a puzzled look and asked, "What lake?"

It only took a second for me to realize why John was confused by my comment. I had forgotten we were in Des Moines, not Cleveland. We were walking along the Des Moines River, which flows south, and definitely does not make it to Lake Erie.

Starting any journey without being certain of your current location is unlikely to get you where you're going. Even worse, it's possible that your first steps could actually take you farther from your final destination. Freeing yourself from the bias of your own experience and preconceptions is the first step in understanding where you are. For organizations and teams wanting to transform their operations to a lean model, finding clues to your current location can be like figuring out if you are in Cleveland or Des Moines. Similarly, it is also best to get an outsider's perspective.

We each understand our world from our own perspective, using our history as a lens through which to interpret everything we see and experience. If you think you are in a certain place, you will instinctively use that understanding to explain everything around you, and your perception of reality could easily leave you looking for the North Star while facing south.

In 2013, a major construction industry publication shared the findings of an industry-wide survey about the application of lean in construction. They asked leaders at dozens of US construction companies how they used lean tools, the impact lean has had on their operations, and the challenges they faced in their lean journeys. For me, the most revealing information from that survey came from two questions: "How advanced are you in your use of lean?" and "How long have you been pursuing lean practices?"

The results showed that companies that had been pursuing lean for the shortest amount of time thought they were the most advanced in their lean practices. Of course, these companies' perceived lean prowess was overblown, a misinterpretation of their current location. The reality was that these companies had an immature understanding of lean principles and they didn't fully grasp what was possible with a lean operation. Their perception of their current position was wrong.

A lean transformation journey is a string of revelations that I often explain with this parable:

A climber is making his way up a mountain and sees only a few climbers ahead of him. Because he sees lots of people coming up the slope behind him, he feels that he's doing well on his journey and outperforming the typical climber. When he sees the summit before him, he feels like he's nearing his objective. Only when he reaches the peak does the climber see the actual summit in the distance with a long stream of climbers ahead of him. Only then does he recognize that he is actually nowhere near the end.

Those who have been climbing for a while know that each accomplishment provides a new vantage point from which to survey the broader landscape and set higher goals. What we imagine is possible and the goals we set for ourselves are influenced by our current perspective. The construction companies from the survey that thought they were near the ultimate goal only believed this because they didn't realize that their mountain peak was merely the first foothill in a much longer journey of learning, discovery, and growth. Experienced climbers also know that reaching the summit is not the final objective either. It is another peak from which the climber will be able to see even farther ahead and once again gain a better understanding of his ultimate objective. To determine your actual location, to truly understand your strengths, shortcomings and the full potential of what lies ahead, it is essential that you gain the perspective of those with a broader vision, ideally those who are ahead of you on the journey. There are several practical ways to accomplish this.

First, engage with the lean design and construction communities to learn what others are doing. There are many organizations where lean practitioners from project-driven organizations share with and learn from one another. We've compiled a list of these organizations and links to their sites at our resource page: LeanProject.com/BetterBuilding. It includes the Lean Construction Institute (LCI), The International Group for Lean Construction (IGLC), and Berkeley's Project Production Systems Laboratory (P2SL), among others. This alphabet soup of organizations provide training, conferences, local meetings, and most importantly, a network of lean thinkers who are intent on improving how design and construction work get done. When you engage with these kinds of organizations by attending meetings, subscribing to newsletters, and joining local chapters, you'll find that there are many others traveling with you. Get involved and build connections here; your view of the world will soon be challenged, your perspective will expand, and your expectations for your own organization will rise.

As you get connected to a broader lean community, remember that the people leading the charge were once in your situation. They are learners on a journey and most of them are eager to help others on their way. Don't hesitate to reach out and build personal connections to those you most admire. If they sense you have an open mind and are eager to learn, they will likely enjoy the connection as much as you do. Instructions for contacting me are included on the resource page link. I'd love to hear about your current circumstances and aspirations for your own growth and improvement.

Second, pay attention to lean progress and thought leaders outside your own industry. I've learned much by following lean leaders in shipbuilding, software development, healthcare, manufacturing, and new product development. While none of these represent my primary business's area of interest in building, I can see many similarities in their struggles and progress. Learning what works in these realms provides insight into what might be effective in my own work and provides inspiration for me to consider new improvements that might be possible. Every story of progress (or failure), whether revolutionary or incremental, expands my personal map of the lean territory and sharpens my own perception of where I stand.

Many organizations start their lean efforts alone, but seek outside help after becoming frustrated with their lack of progress. This is why my last bit of advice is to get expert help. With the support of an experienced outside consultant, you will gain insight into the progress made by others in your industry and clarity about the challenges and opportunities you face. An expert can help you attain the early summits quickly, extend the benefits over time, and become a trusted guide for a much longer and more rewarding journey.

When we partner with new clients, our first task is to help them better understand themselves. By challenging their current paradigms, we open the door to new thinking and greater possibilities. This often includes an assessment of their current situation, which reveals intrinsic barriers to change and the leadership gaps that are preventing them from making real progress. While many companies have been aware of these fundamental problems for years, it's only when they accept that their own perspective and biases are blocking their progress, and agree to deliberately address them with outside help, that the log jam can be broken up and they start to get into a flow.

Set Clear Goals

In lean thinking, the ultimate destination is never achieved. Lean is a never-ending journey that continuously challenges you to improve and achieve more. This might sound like an exhausting way to live or to operate a company, but in practice, it generates a lot more energy than it consumes. In this context the primary purpose of setting long-term goals is not to establish the ultimate end state, but to establish the direction.

Elon Musk's company, SpaceX, has the following mission statement:

> *SpaceX designs, manufactures and launches advanced rockets and spacecraft. The company was founded in 2002 to revolutionize space technology, with the ultimate goal of enabling people to live on other planets.*[20]

To accomplish this, it's set a goal of establishing a colony of one million people on Mars within fifty to one hundred years. This goal, whether it's ultimately achieved or not, has the primary purpose of setting the direction of the organization. The company's near-term actions are informed by the long-term vision. In this way, actions are coordinated in alignment with a compelling purpose.

Designing and launching an economical heavy-lift rocket capable of transporting 200 passengers is not only in alignment with the long-term objective, but also spurs technology improvements along the way that help the company achieve its immediate commercial needs— economically transporting satellites into orbit for its customers. SpaceX just achieved a big technological step by successfully landing a rocket softly back on earth using thrust. This allows for reuse of rockets and dramatically reduces the cost of each mission. It's an

---

[20] "About SpaceX," SpaceX.com (website), accessed June 11, 2018, http://www.spacex.com/about.)

important step in economizing space flight, one that NASA never even attempted.

When you think about defining a direction, set a tangible vision of your future state that acts as a guide for your everyday actions. However lofty and aggressive, use the details of the objective to steer your progress. One construction company was early in their lean journey and wanted to provide a consistent driving purpose for continued learning and organizational improvement. By looking at the companies they admired most, they saw that they had fallen behind the industry in adopting lean thinking, including a relatively new lean project delivery method called Integrated Project Delivery (IPD).[21] The practice had been around for a few years, and had proven to provide a more consistent and higher value design and construction experience through shorter schedules and lower prices. However, to implement IPD requires a new kind of relationship between project owners, contractors, designers, and trade contractors. It utilizes new contracting formats, including dramatically different approaches to collaboration, allocation of risk, and ultimately, the way all project participants earn profit. Although the company had no customers interested in using IPD at the time, and there were few examples of IPD projects in their region, they established the goal of participating in an IPD project within three years.

This aspirational goal set in motion a series of experiments and learning that benefited the company daily, before they actually participated in an IPD project. The truth is, even if they never ended up participating in an actual IPD project, the mere act of driving toward achieving that goal caused them to learn practical lean methods to plan and manage work more efficiently; to build new, highly collaborative relationships with their key trade and design

---

[21] IPD and the other lean tools mentioned here are explained in more detail in the next chapter.

partners; to experiment with new contract terms that better align the financial goals of all project participants; and a host of other benefits.

Through their efforts, they gained a reputation as a contractor intently focused on providing more value to owners and a better work experience for trade and design partners. Internally, they created a culture of challenge and achievement that has energized their people and attracted new talent to the company.

Expect Resistance

Many organizations make the mistake of thinking that change management is a mechanical process that only requires deciding what to do and making sure everyone in the organization knows how to do it. We don't have to look far for evidence that this perception is way off base. The historical track record of failure in implementing organizational change speaks for itself. In fact, a recent survey shows that 55 percent of executives feel their organizations are ineffective at introducing change as part of strategy deployment. Only 7 percent felt their organizations had an approach that was very effective.[22]

Applying lean to an organization requires a change in the way an organization thinks and acts, which can only happen when its people change the way they think and act. If you've ever tried to change a personal habit, you know how difficult that can be—eating less, exercising more, quitting smoking, saving money, and spending more quality time with family are changes that are easy to decide to do, yet can be difficult to accomplish. Changing the behavior and thinking of an organization means getting everyone to change deeply embedded habits at the same time. It's easy to see why companies can be overwhelmed by the prospect.

---

[22] "Why Good Strategies Fail: Lessons for the C-Suite," *The Economist Intelligence Unit Limited*, 2013, https://www.pmi.org/-/media/pmi/documents/public/pdf/learning/thought-leadership/why-good-strategies-fail-report.pdf.

The best place to start is to recognize that while the process might be simple, people are complicated. Individuals have their own barriers to change, reasons for holding on to old mindsets, and personal interests that can prevent a shift in the organization. The book *Switch*[23] by Chip and Dan Heath provides a great analogy for dealing with this complexity.

The authors explain three aspects of change through the analogy of an elephant and its rider on a path toward a specific destination—the place you want to be as a result of a change. The rider represents the logical thinking part of every person and organization. To change the rider, you need to explain the desired new behavior, the reasons why it's important, and how to do it. Getting the rider on your side is a matter of imparting understanding and building capability. This is the part of change management that most people understand.

The elephant represents the more complicated emotional side of every person and group. While the rider may want to go in a new direction, he has little chance of getting there if the elephant has a different idea. Redirecting the elephant requires removing fear, instilling confidence, and providing motivation to go in a new direction. When planning for your own change, plan to engage with the emotional side of individuals to remove their fear and apprehension about the new world you're asking them to enter. At the same time, provide them with personal motivation to behave in a new way. This usually means breaking down the change into smaller, less "risky" components and building in some quick wins. This helps individuals feel safe about trying new things and lets them know it's OK to struggle, raise concerns, and even to fail along the way. Only when individuals have a sense of control and confidence can they become truly committed

---

[23] Chip Heath and Dan Heath, *Switch: How to Change Things When Change is Hard* (New York: Crown Publishing Group, 2010)

to the change that is so important for the organization. Leaders must understand that if you want people to take care of the company, you must be willing to take care of them in the process. This is the most difficult (and neglected) part of personal and organizational change and, when change efforts fail, this is often the cause.

Finally, the elephant's path represents the organizational and social cues that help the elephant and rider move confidently in the right direction. Establishing the path for an organization helps everyone understand what is expected and what behavior is (and is not) acceptable. This path, which is made evident through standards, visual cues, and the modeling of new behaviors, makes the direction clear so people can see when they've taken a wrong turn. Creating a clear path defines the new norms or system in which people will be operating as a result of the change.

Every successful change requires change in people, including you. Expect that you will encounter resistance, both inside and out, and be prepared to work through it by addressing the many complicated facets of human nature, your own included. By addressing all three parts of the puzzle—the rider, the elephant, and the path—you will be in a position to guide yourself and your organization through a challenging process with confidence.

Practice Leadership at Every Level

Effective change leadership requires effective leaders. However, these leaders are not only located in the boardroom. They reside at every level of a lean organization.

For most project-driven companies, the transition to lean thinking requires a redistribution of leadership and responsibility to all levels, away from the central authoritarian leadership that's typical in many traditional organizations. This doesn't necessarily mean that the entire organizational chart has to be overturned on day one, but it does mean that leaders at the top need to learn how to distribute their authority and the responsibility for the company's success to all levels.

There is no better place to start this reallocation of leadership than with the management of the change effort itself. By leading the change process in a lean way and distributing responsibility for its success to all levels, you can accomplish three things: learn how to lead in this new lean way, develop the leadership capabilities of more people, and set a powerful example of the new behavior that will carry the company forward.

Since the transition happens through a series of learning experiments, use a leadership structure for any new program that mimics the look and behavior of the lean approach. In my example of the construction company that established the goal of working on a successful IPD project within three years, the structure of the team responsible for that goal should demonstrate the new thinking the organization intends to instill. And it's critically important this type of transition is led by the operational leaders at each level, not by lean champions, coaches, or consultants. Those experts should provide guidance and advice without taking responsibility for the success of the effort as this would remove the responsibility from the operational leaders, and let them off the hook for the learning and growth that they must personally achieve for the effort to succeed.

The responsibility for a long-term goal such as this rests with the organization's leaders, but that does not mean that those leaders do the work of change on their own. The top-level leaders, as part of meeting their objectives, should clearly define the goals to their immediate reports—the next level of leadership in the company. The process is the same one I explained for strategy deployment in Chapter 1. Once the goals for the change initiative are clear, the next level leaders are responsible for developing specific shorter-term objectives that align with the goal. After a back-and-forth negotiation, the next level leaders, armed with clear objectives that they have personally committed to achieving, repeat this process with their reports and so on, creating change leaders from each level of the organization to the next. Each time the broad objectives are clarified and understood by next level, and specific targets are set and agreed upon.

As the work of change progresses, the results get reported in the reverse order. Each level provides information to (and requests help from) the next higher level of the organization. This leads to a negotiation about what should be done to adjust the current approach and provides a clear understanding of the progress to all levels and ultimately to the leader who is responsible for the overall direction and success of the change effort. Linking leaders from one level to the next in this way creates a streamlined path for objectives and support to move from top management to the front lines, and for commitments, results, and requests for help to move just as quickly from the front lines back to the CEO's desk.

When people are first asked to participate in this type of planning and execution model they are often surprised by the level of understanding and commitment required. It's very simple to be told what to do and nod in agreement. It is much more challenging to be asked, "What can your team do to help us make this difficult change and achieve our goals?" As soon as the conversation starts, people realize that they are in a new world where their contributions will directly impact success. People often try to revert to old paradigms and respond with something like "I'm not sure, what do you think I should do?" In a lean environment, this type of response will only be met with more questions, and eventually the individual realizes they must take responsibility for their part of the program, understand fully how they fit into the overall effort, and make commitments about what they will contribute to its success. The role of leaders at each level is to empower and challenge their people, and ensure full alignment from one level to the next while simultaneously developing individual capabilities and delivering results.

Use change initiatives to create these strong links from one level of leadership to the next over time, and leaders will learn to mentor those who work for them and request help from those who are in the best position to provide it. The leadership structure will continue to evolve and everyone's leadership capabilities will continue to improve. You will be living the principles of the Better Building model even as you travel along your transformation journey.

Change Routines to Change Thinking

I'm not sure who originally said it, but a friend once told me "It's easier to behave your way into new thinking than to think your way to new behaviors." This statement epitomizes the final principle of our change management philosophy.

We are all, by nature, creatures of habit. We use routines to help us accomplish our daily tasks in a way that provides predictability and consistency. These routines govern every part of our lives—from the time we set our alarm clocks in the morning, to the route we drive to get to the jobsite, to the way we assemble and turn in time sheets and status reports to our boss. Routines are valuable because they eliminate the need for us to think and make decisions about every move we make, and allow us to accomplish the things that we do on a regular basis with relative ease. They speed up our work and free up our mental capacity for dealing with more challenging, less repetitive decisions. Routines take time to establish, but once there, they become deeply ingrained in the way we function which is also why they are so hard to change.

When people and companies want to change how they think, it's often helpful to begin by changing some routines. One example happened on a design project where the meetings were notoriously ineffective and ran on for what seemed like forever. The team leaders were frustrated by their inability to change the culture around meetings, even though they had sent emails and made speeches about the importance of concise, effective meetings. The project participants had developed some bad habits like showing up late, saving important information until the end of the meeting, and inviting many more people than necessary, all of which were acting as barriers to the new way of conducting meetings and working together collaboratively.

We worked with the project leader to design a few basic routines that would change the group's thinking about meetings. They were able to change everything by modeling three new behaviors for the group:

1. Only invite those who are absolutely necessary to a meeting.

2. Start on time and follow an agenda.

3. Finish every meeting on time.

While changing an entire project culture around meetings and collaboration is a major undertaking, making the three behavior changes was easy. First, the meeting leader reviewed the invite list, which included about thirty people, and indicated the eight people that were required. We changed all the others' status to "optional attendees." At the first meeting after the change, only five of the required eight people showed up on time. Rather than starting the meeting anyway, the leader called the missing required attendees and got two more into the room. After trying to reach the final required attendee for another ten minutes, the leader cancelled the meeting. This new behavior shocked the group a bit and they grumbled about wasting time coming to a meeting that ultimately never happened. But the result was that the required attendees began arriving on time to every meeting. If they needed to miss a meeting or be late, they'd let someone know in advance and arrange for a surrogate to take their place.

The leader also created a standard agenda for the meeting and posted it on the wall in the room. It listed four topics and each was allocated fifteen minutes of the one-hour meeting. After reaching the time limit for a given topic, the leader would say, "if there's more to discuss we'll have to pick it up next time," and move on in the agenda. Once again, people were originally frustrated that they couldn't follow their habit of rambling endlessly on one particular topic. Over time, they learned that their discussion would be quick, and much of the needless chatter and complaining went away. If someone had serious issues to bring up, they came prepared with a concise explanation and brief requests for help from the leader or other meeting participants.

Finally, at the scheduled conclusion time the leader would close the meeting and leave the room.

The new meeting routines implemented by the leader changed behaviors first and then changed thinking. Meeting participants recognized that they had to come to this meeting prepared and ready to engage in serious discussion as soon as the meeting started. They knew that they could count on important work getting done and that the meeting would conclude on time. They knew that if they needed something from one of the other participants, they could count on them to be present and prepared for the discussion.

Everyone who participated agreed that the three new behaviors resulted in the most effective meeting in the organization and the most valuable hour of their week. They were amazed at how much more they accomplished with fewer people, in less time, and with much less frustration. They adopted new thinking about how to work together and began to apply their new understanding to other meetings.

While making a lean transformation is about changing thinking, it can be much faster to simply change some of the routines that are common among your team. Pick a few that you think can make a difference and give it a try. You might be surprised how impactful it can be.

8

Lean Tools for Project Work

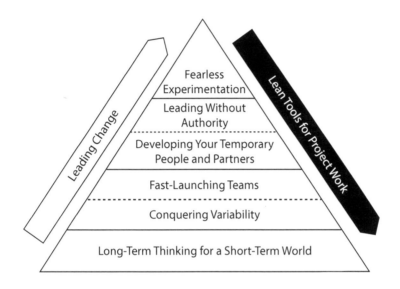

MANY YEARS AGO AFTER my wife and I purchased our first home, we decided to add a substantial addition. I enjoy working with my hands and I'm good with a hammer, so I was determined to do much of the work myself, starting with the rough framing. For my wife and me, it was about learning to do something new, the anticipation of pride in our completed project, and the fact that we could afford much more house if we did it ourselves.

My father had just retired after a long career as a carpenter, and he was excited that I wanted to tackle the construction myself. He knew the sense of pride that he'd gotten from his own work, and that it would be a great learning experience for me. He was an expert at residential framing and offered to spend the first few weekends to set me off on the right track. However, I had already recruited a couple strong, young friends to help out and was really reluctant to accept help from my dad. I didn't want to draft him back into the world of manual labor at his age, and I also thought there wasn't a lot he could add. I'd picked up a couple books on house construction from the library and talked to some friends who had done similar projects. I was a structural engineer who had designed many complex structures in the past and knew that framing a house was pretty straightforward. I made sure I had the right hammer, saw, level, and chalk line. I was ready to start.

On the Saturday that we started framing, my friends and I started at 6:00 a.m. We had received the lumber order on Friday and reviewed the framing plans the night before. We started the morning with a discussion about which wall to frame first. That was followed by a discussion about how the corners should be insulated since the corner cavities would be inaccessible after the adjoining wall was erected. Next we planned how the stud spacing would accommodate the plumbing and ductwork without causing complications for those trades later. We planned how we'd verify the walls were plumb and the structure was square as we moved along. The conversation continued, working out one detail after the next, like any good engineer would do.

My dad showed up (more or less uninvited) at 8:00 a.m. I was surprised and let him know that we had things well under control, but once on site, the carpenter foreman in him took over. He laid out the first three walls, including the corners and stud spacing to accommodate insulation, plumbing, and HVAC ducts. His confidence and understanding about every detail was instinctive, and he sometimes couldn't explain why he was doing things the way he was. He just knew what was right and knew what had worked on dozens of similar projects. I never once doubted his guidance and of course, the layout and details were right on the money. By the end of the day we had the entire floor framed and ready for the deck the next day. I gained a new respect for expertise (in any field) and recognized how naive I was to think that I could understand this new world simply by studying it and having the right tools.

In the end, my dad's guidance allowed us to get the framing done in half the time. More important, the framing was done right, and we avoided all sorts of pitfalls with insulating, sheathing, and mechanicals as a result. No amount of reading, discussion, or new tools could give me the experience and understanding of an expert carpenter. While my inexperience made it hard for me to see my own shortcomings, my dad's expertise made them obvious to him. I often think of this episode when clients want to load themselves with the latest tools as they work to make lean changes to their operations.

At our consulting company, we are always thrilled when we get a call for help from a new client. Of course, this kind of a call represents new work for our business, but that's not why we get excited. What makes it exciting is that often the person on the other end of the phone is peeking into a new world for the first time—cautiously exploring what this idea of lean is all about and how it might help their project or business. At times they are skeptical about the success stories they've heard from others in the industry and they've decided to explore it for themselves. Many are beginning to think about lean for the first time. Others have been at it for a while and are feeling stuck in their progress; looking for the missing ingredient that will cause lean to make a real difference for them and their company. We are truly fortunate to have these adventurous, driven individuals as our clients.

One of the most common requests from potential new clients is, "Can you teach us to use _____?" The blank is filled in with any number of lean "tools" that are becoming increasingly popular in the industry. I'm using the term tools in this context, to refer to the techniques and processes that are applied to the work. Just like a saw is a tool used to cut a board, or a stoplight is a tool used to control traffic, lean tools help us accomplish work in a specific way. The request often continues with "We really only need a day or two of training and we should be able to take it from there." Our initial response is almost always "Sorry, we don't do training on lean tools alone."

What we mean is that we don't do training on lean tools separate from a purpose and intention to learn and grow as an organization, or separate from understanding that in order for lean tools to work, they must accompany new thinking and behaviors. Our reasoning is simple: training the mechanics of tools in isolation does not work, and we don't want to waste everyone's time and our client's money, or stake our reputation, on an effort that we know will fail. Of course, lean tools are an important part of organizational improvement and ultimately of a transformation toward a truly lean learning organization, but you cannot lead the charge by learning tools alone.

In the Better Building model, the "Lean Tools for Project Work" arrow indicates that tools are there to support a new way of thinking and help the thinking take hold. The arrow starts at the value-added work—the core work that the company completes to meet the needs of its customers—and moves through the layers of the organization. The tools are one way that the new thinking becomes tangible and supports the overall strategy and philosophy—the mindset of the organization.

As you work to shift your thinking and behavior toward a lean mindset and consider which lean tools can support the change, recognize that there are two aspects to every tool. First, there is the mechanical part—how you track the information, generate plans, and report results. This aspect of most tools is pretty straightforward. The other aspect—the human side—is much trickier.

Even though many lean tools have been in use for decades and are proven effective, I've seen good lean tools applied in a way that actually takes a team backward by reinforcing dysfunctional command and control thinking. The poor outcome is not due to the tool, but its poor implementation. Unfortunately, once someone believes they have been "burned by a lean tool," the prospect of getting them engaged for another try becomes twice as challenging.

That's why before you implement a tool, it's vital that you answer certain questions: How will the tool promote more collaboration and personal development? How will it reinforce the right behaviors and make people more likely to bring problems to the surface? How will it create a spirit of experimentation and learning in the team? In addition, find a resource, an expert, to act as a guide while you learn how to use the tool for your purpose in your specific circumstances.

For our purposes here, I've selected only a handful of tools that are most applicable to the project-driven world and most directly support a shift in thinking. For each one listed, I've provided three pieces of information: a brief overview of the tool—what it does and how it does it; how the tool supports a shift toward lean thinking; and a few tips, tricks, or words of caution to consider before you start. For the reasons explained at the start of the chapter, this is not intended to be a how-to manual for each tool. Instead, consider it a peek into each one with an eye toward understanding its function and how it might help you meet your objectives and support the culture you intend to create. View this listing much like you would a restaurant menu to help you choose your meal and not like a cookbook where you would turn to learn the recipe.

The Last Planner® System (Including Pull Planning)

The Last Planner® System[24] (LPS) is by far the most requested and commonly used lean tool in the design and construction industry; and probably the tool most often misapplied. The term "Last Planner" refers to a person—the one who is closest to the work with responsibility for planning and management. In building projects, the Last Planner could be a foreman, superintendent, design manager, or owner's representative. In reality, every project has many Last Planners. LPS provides a structured approach to planning and managing the work of a project with the goal of creating reliable workflow. It uses five key elements in a coordinated system to accomplish project objectives while fostering learning and improvement weekly and even daily.

Last Planner® System
Should-Can-Will-Did Planning

Creating and maintaining reliable workflow

---

[24] Last Planner® is a registered trademark of Lean Construction Institute.

I think of it like this. Imagine the ideal week of work on a project. A week where every trade gets exactly what they want done; there are no conflicts between trades; there are no unexpected surprises to disrupt the work; all the necessary information, materials and equipment arrive in time; the team's productivity, safety, and quality are the best you've ever seen; there is no overtime required; the costs are lower than you ever thought possible; everyone on the project has a great work experience; and the owner is absolutely delighted. Sounds pretty good, right?

In the Last Planner® System, the team strives to make that dream a reality—the best week ever. Then the process is repeated every week to make it happen over and over again for the entire duration of the project. I know it seems impossible to have that kind of an impact on project work, but we've seen this powerful shift happen many times and have heard tradespeople, foremen, superintendents, project managers, and owners describe the transformation caused by the Last Planner® System as an experience they never thought was possible.

LPS is a great way to begin a shift in thinking at the project level. When implementing LPS, we teach leaders at every level how to be expert facilitators and mentors to those who work for them; raising expectations and developing their capabilities in a way that empowers them to contribute more to the project's success. It builds trust and confidence among the team and creates a culture where individuals watch out for each other while delivering what's best for the project.

Successful LPS is also based on learning to make and get reliable commitments from teammates. Seeing reliable workflow as the result of a network of commitments takes time to learn and creates a new level of collaboration and coordination among the team. Learning to make and get reliable commitments as part of LPS changes individual behavior and makes team members more effective. Individuals often step up as leaders in a broader cultural shift in their own organizations, beyond just the work on a single project.

When learning to use LPS, stick with the fundamentals. We see many companies start with an LPS software package or elaborate pre-printed notes and display boards. Our best implementations start with very simple spreadsheets, lots of information on whiteboards, and very simple meeting structures and agendas. Learn to use these "in public," in view of the entire project team so that all recognize it's OK to be a learner and ask questions. It makes everyone more comfortable with the process and makes the buy-in to a new way of operating much more likely.

One mistake we see with LPS is that teams want to use just one part of the process rather than all elements as a coordinated system. Pull planning—a key part of LPS used to collaboratively plan one phase of a project—is important, but cannot deliver the benefits of LPS on its own. In fact, we typically establish strong Weekly Work Plans and set the process for Weekly Coordination Meetings before we worry about pull planning.

Finally, remember that the power of LPS comes from a change in behavior. If it is used to drive performance in a command-and-control style, it will get the same results as your current approach. If it becomes just a new set of forms and metrics to "hold others accountable" rather than empower them to make real commitments, you are thinking about it all wrong. You should expect that your current mindset will be challenged as you learn to use LPS, and that you'll feel like a novice in a new world. If you don't feel like a beginner, it's a sure sign that you haven't left your comfort zone.[25]

---

[25] Note that LPS can be as effective in project design work as it is in construction. However, it's best to make some modifications to better accommodate the cycle of unknowns, discovery, and design that is inherent in design work. We've had good success with a blending of agile and LPS approaches that we call Responsibility-based Project Delivery™ (RbPD). The approach combines short design sprints with weekly planning and daily check-ins to align a team to project objectives while coordinating their work to achieve reliable workflow in design

A3 Problem Solving

The term A3 refers to a single piece of paper. In the United States, it's referred to as tabloid size, or 11" x 17". The idea with A3 problem solving is to concisely explain a problem and get to its root cause before making and implementing a plan for solving it. While the immediate purpose is to solve a real problem, the process creates a dynamic for learning that empowers people to take responsibility for solving problems and making improvements all the time.

The A3 process is really a conversation between the problem solver (or problem solving team) and their mentor, which happens through a visual tool, the A3. The person responsible for solving the problem presents the issue as concisely and clearly as possible. The reviewer asks for clarifications and often challenges the assumptions that are baked into the first draft. Through this back-and-forth negotiation, the presenter and reviewer both gain a deeper understanding of the situation and arrive at a much stronger plan for solving the problem. It is a tool for developing people while solving problems and supporting the key lean principles of continuous improvement and respect for people.

When using A3 problem solving, focus on the conversation, not just the A3 report itself. The report should be a relic of the conversation, documenting the process and the plan so that it can be shared with others. It also provides a structured approach to the conversation itself, proving a standard way to teach it to others and get the right conversations happening throughout the organization. Too often, we see companies out on their own generating dozens of A3 reports—each one created by one individual with little feedback from others, and little learning or coaching. It's truly a missed opportunity.

Visual Management (Including 5S Programs)

The idea of visual management is to make every process obvious to those who work in it and those who manage it so that the standards are easy to understand and follow. Think of visual management as a way for everyone to know the score. Are we meeting our objectives, are we following our process, are there any problems for us to address? There are many ways to use visual management, some of which I've discussed earlier in the book. A 5S program is a great way to apply visual management to any physical workspace and is ideal for a building site.

The term 5S originates from Japanese terms that are translated somewhat awkwardly into English:

1. Sort

2. Straighten

3. Shine/Sweep

4. Standardize

5. Sustain

The process provides a great way to organize a work area or even an entire project. Classic examples of 5S are seen in techniques like "shadow boards," the pegboards you might see in a workshop that include a silhouette of each tool. It lets everyone know where each tool belongs and lets you know immediately if a tool is missing. In an office environment 5S can define how you store supplies, organize files, or deal with shared information on a computer network or email server. It allows teams to follow simple organizational standards and maintain structure in a way that speeds up work and eliminates wasted time hunting for things or generally dealing with disorganization.

Many companies implement structured 5S programs on every project site or in every office. This encourages individuals to become engaged with lean transformation and empowers them to take steps within their immediate control. It's very impactful when someone can be part of an effort to standardize how tools are organized in a job box or how equipment is bundled when it's shipped to and from the company yard. When a plumber can design their own work cart or an administrator can design their own desk layout, they sense that making improvements is important and they know that they are expected to be part of the program. They can take pride in their own accomplishments and are often eager to participate in bigger efforts that affect the organization more broadly.

When using 5S in your organization, set an example for others with your own behavior. Even if your own 5S activities are limited, use them to show what 5S is all about. This is much more effective than explaining the 5S terms or telling others what they should do while failing to practice it yourself. Your living example can create an energy that gets others involved and brings standards and improvements to the forefront without lecturing or dictating new behaviors. You'll have much more success if 5S is something that people want to do rather than what they are told to do.

Along these same lines, it's critical that 5S ideas are generated by the people and not thrust upon them. If 5S improvements are developed by those not directly involved, they can be seen as restrictive and unresponsive to the needs of those who are asked to implement them. Ask everyone in your company to improve their own workspace, and ask them to work in teams for project-wide or company-wide improvements. You'll find this process proliferates lean thinking, facilitates personal growth and satisfaction, and provides better results for all concerned.

Quick Wins

Like a 5S program, a Quick Wins program is a great way to involve all the people in an organization or a project to make improvements as part of a lean culture shift. As the name implies, the idea is to get people to experience success quickly by making improvements in their own work. When they get acknowledged for the successes, it encourages buy-in for the new expectation of continuous improvement. When the ideas are shared openly and the best ideas are publicly acknowledged, a culture of improvement is created from the grass-roots level.

The powerful thing about a Quick Wins program is that it builds momentum off the successes of "normal people." It is not driven by leadership or a mandate from on high, rather it is a true grassroots movement to make things better. The lean concept of empowering individuals can have no stronger manifestation than a culture where everyone improves all the time.

The idea of getting people involved is often misinterpreted as a suggestion system where people are asked to submit their ideas for improvement without the responsibility to make their own improvements. I worked with a company that (before we were involved) purchased dozens of "lean suggestion boxes" that were prominently displayed in each office and on every project. These came complete with forms to fill out that described the improvement idea including the amount of money that it would save the company. In the end, the boxes remained mostly empty. The few suggestions submitted were either way too elaborate and expensive to actually implement or more of a complaint for someone else to deal with. Little or no improvement resulted.

Instead, a Quick Wins program is designed to encourage everyone to make improvements within their own authority and share the results with others in an open forum. In Chapter 6 I shared a story about a laborer's experiment with an improved method for snow removal. That type of improvement epitomizes what is possible with a Quick Wins program. In the same way, an architect can display their biggest design challenges on the wall to invite conversation and open input from the team, or a plumber can design a jig for aligning pipes before welding. Both the architect and the plumber can make these changes without approval from a manager, and both examples require minimal financial investment. When the improvement ideas are shared with others, it creates a culture that encourages everyone to join in and try their own improvements. Keep the process simple and recognize good ideas. Let the people do the rest.

Choosing by Advantages Decision-Making

Choosing by Advantages (CBA) is a decision-making process that has been adopted by many lean projects and organizations, especially in the project-driven environment. It helps teams make sound decisions with confidence by determining the relative advantage of one alternative over another, and it has variations that work with every type of decision. Teams require a bit of education and practice to get the hang of it, but those that adopt the approach make decisions more quickly, more collaboratively, and with greater confidence while eliminating much of second-guessing and circling back that plague many project teams. The beauty of CBA is that it allows a team to compare the advantages of unrelated attributes of different alternatives on a common scale of importance. For example, it can be used to compare several separate building design concepts for multiple unrelated factors from aesthetics, to energy efficiency, to occupant comfort. It can also help a team compare the cost implications of alternatives to ensure the best value option is selected.

Adopting CBA for decision-making puts several lean principles to work. First, it requires that decisions are made on accurate, first-hand information. This may seem like an obvious necessity for any decision-making process, but we often find that's not the case. When teams apply CBA for the first time, they often realize that they have not done the homework needed to make a well-informed decision. Like many lean practices, CBA reinforces the idea that sometimes you have to go slow to go fast, taking the time to get it right the first time.

CBA also strengthens teamwork by creating open discussions where individuals share their concerns and work to understand the perspective of others. This is quite different from traditional decision-making approaches that rely on lobbying others to support your wishes and encourage individuals to "dig in" and protect their own needs over the needs of the broader project or organization. In this way, CBA allows a team to put the interests of the whole ahead of the interests of any one individual.

Learning to use CBA requires the adoption of a new common language to bring a team together. To have the right conversation, it's critical that you use the right language. CBA has very specific definitions and uses for words like alternative, attribute, criteria, advantage, and importance. By adopting a disciplined use of these terms, a team can make a lot of progress toward the effective use of CBA. If a team gets sloppy with the terms, it often leads to a sloppy implementation of CBA that fails to provide consistently strong results.

In addition, it's important to recognize that CBA is a group exercise. Do not try to make a CBA decision in isolation and present it to the team for their acceptance. They will never gain a full understanding of the issue or give their full buy-in to the outcome if they are not part of the development. The result can be a return to the second-guessing that's typical without CBA.

Integrated Project Delivery

Integrated Project Delivery (IPD) is probably the biggest improvement in the process of design and construction since the invention of the steam shovel. IPD is a contractual arrangement that replaces the traditional contract structures of design-bid-build and other more progressive approaches used in negotiated project agreements. The key difference is that IPD relies on a relational rather than a transactional agreement; assembling a team that agrees to behave in a certain way to accomplish a common goal.

IPD projects rely on several key components that differ from traditional delivery models:

- All parties sign the same agreement (owner, designers, contractors and key trades)

- Design and construction partners are engaged much earlier in the design process

- Shared risk, contingency, and reward (if project objectives are met)

- Partners are guaranteed payment for all costs (cannot lose money on the project)

- Waiver of rights to make claims against other team members

- Open-book accounting where true costs are transparently shared

- Target cost is set significantly below the expected cost based on similar projects

- Decisions are made by the project team, not just the owner

The practical outcome of this style of agreement is that team members are truly aligned around the project objectives. The contract structure rewards individual members for doing what's best for the project and removes the incentive for putting their own interests first. In addition, it allows for the "frictionless movement" of work and money from one party to the next without the need for a change order. Imagine that the team decides that the HVAC contractor is best qualified to complete the BIM modeling and layout for all the trades. An IPD allows for the HVAC contractor to get paid for this extra work, relieves him of the liability if there were to be a problem, and allows the team to make this change without delay. The change in delivery approach allows projects to achieve costs and schedules that were once unimaginable while delivering on the owner's highest priorities for the project.

Our consulting firm has been part of many IPD projects, and we were involved with some of the earliest efforts where the key concepts were developed. At that time, it was determined that the new project delivery approach would rely on five key principles. These "five big ideas" were used as a guide to transform how projects get designed and built. These ideas come directly from lean thinking.

1. Collaborate, Really Collaborate
2. Optimize the Whole, Not the Parts
3. Tightly Couple Learning with Action
4. Increase Relatedness
5. Project as a Network of Commitments

Because these concepts are built into the IPD approach, the approach itself requires lean thinking to make it work. Even team members who aren't familiar with lean concepts learn about them as they work on an IPD project. When general contractors, trade contractors, and designers participate in an IPD project, the experience often kick-starts a broader lean transformation in their own companies.

As Integrated Project Delivery becomes more popular in the industry, we are seeing two unfortunate trends. First, project owners who don't understand lean are adopting select portions of the IPD approach. They want to get the benefits of the new model without giving up on old styles of management. The result, often referred to as IPD-ish Project Delivery, is a watered-down project organization where the owner doesn't really empower the team, or guarantee payment for all costs, or align the team around the best interests of the project. The outcomes are muted at best, and the combined result is a team that doesn't understand real lean thinking and becomes disillusioned about the idea that real progress can be made in project delivery.

The second trend is that some project teams view IPD as a purely contractual shift rather than a shift in team behavior. Remember that IPD is a contracting style that allows teams to behave in a more collaborative, lean way. However, an IPD agreement cannot cause an uncollaborative team that's stuck in a traditional mindset to behave in a lean way. The most successful IPD projects that I've been involved with—saving 30% of labor costs, eliminating quality and safety issues, and drastically shortening schedules—have been accomplished by teams that are eager to collaborate at a higher level, make major improvements to their processes, and apply lean thinking. Adopting an IPD approach enables an ambitious team to behave in ways that are impossible under traditional contracts. The desire for lean improvement drives the change toward Integrated Project Delivery, not the other way around.

Conclusion

As you think about practical ways to launch lean thinking in your team or organization, you can't go wrong considering any of the tools described in this chapter. Each one provides immediate benefits to any project and supports a shift toward lean thinking in its own way. Take some time to learn about these tools, and don't be afraid to experiment a bit. As you do, find a guide—someone who has first-hand experience with these tools and can help you avoid pitfalls and make quick progress without burning up a lot of energy, time, and money on wrong turns. Having a trusted guide will give you the ability to move with confidence and speed toward a new, brighter future in your project-driven world.

———

About the Author

Klaus Lemke is a thought leader in the building industry. His consulting company is the premier partner for those who want to advance their organizations through continuous improvement and respect for people.

Klaus started his career as a structural engineer and EPC project manager in the petroleum industry, where he first learned about Deming's Total Quality Management, partnering and continuous improvement. Switching to general contracting in 1996, Klaus was disappointed with the disconnected, siloed nature of the AEC industry and began looking for a better way. Klaus connected with Greg Howell in 2005 and began applying lean techniques in his own company.

After years of studying lean thinking and practicing lean tactics, Klaus joined LeanProject as Managing Principal. He and his partners have helped countless teams adopt the new behaviors and thinking required to dramatically shorten schedules, reduce cost, increase safety and improve the experience of project work.

Using a humble coaching style while maintaining high expectations for his students, Klaus goes beyond the mechanical, process-oriented side of lean and leverages the human nature behind successful teams and cultural transformation. His ability to connect with people at all levels keeps him in high demand as a speaker, trainer, coach and change agent for his clients.

Klaus thrives on connecting with lean thinkers who want to transform the building industry. You can contact him at *http://leanproject.com/BetterBuilding.*

About
Lean Project Consulting, Inc.

◐ LeanProject PUBLISHING

As the leading consulting firm focused on applying lean to the building industry, LeanProject has helped countless projects and organizations make the shift form traditional to lean thinking. The new thinking and behaviors create reliable workflow and a spirit of continuous improvement, which help projects achieve better results than many thought possible.

Applying lean principles to project work is as much about leadership and culture change as it is about lean tools and techniques. LeanProject helps organizations and individuals increase their competence as lean practitioners through a combination of training and coaching while acting as a trusted partner for your lean journey. As an outside resource, they can help you assess your existing situation, challenge your current thinking, and expect more from yourself and your organization.

LeanProject continues to lead the industry with innovative offerings for leadership development and organizational transformation specifically targeted at the building industry. Whether you intend to implement lean on a single project or transform your entire organization, LeanProject has been there before and can act as a trusted guide for your lean journey. For more information about speakers, workshops, and coaching programs visit *www.leanproject.com* or email us at *inquire@leanproject.com*.

Made in the USA
Lexington, KY
23 September 2018